Don't Limit Your Senses

SOUND AND THE LEARNING ENVIRONMENT

ISBN 91-974193-1-1

Production: Saint-Gobain Ecophon AB, Hyllinge, Sweden
Smash Palace AB, Helsingborg, Sweden
Golden Apple Communications AB, Stockholm, Sweden
Lennart Persson Grafisk Formgivning, Nyhamnsläge, Sweden

Repro & print: Ljungbergs Tryckeri, Klippan, Sweden

Don't Limit Your Senses

Daycare centres, schools, colleges, corporate training...
Added together, educational establishments often constitute a country's largest workplace.
Teaching and learning place high personal demands on teachers and students alike.
The physical environment should not be an obstacle, but unfortunately it often is.

Education is fundamental to the development of the individual and of society. The requirements for the working environment in the field of education should therefore be set at a high level. Learning requires a great deal of attention as the information is not only new, but has to be heard correctly, processed, understood and remembered.

The indoor environment has a major impact on our ability to process and pass on knowledge.

Problems of noise, air quality, temperature and light are well-known to many of those who study, teach or perform other work in a learning environment.

"Don't Limit Your Senses" highlights common problems with the indoor environment, explains the concepts involved and suggests measures to be taken. The book focuses on room acoustics in particular, with one chapter offering advice and recommendations on acoustics for various types of room.

"Don't Limit Your Senses" is perhaps not the kind of book you would read from cover to cover, so the content has been divided into chapters and sections, which can stand alone. However, "Sound in the learning environment" is a key chapter. If you are interested in understanding the concepts and issues concerning room acoustics and the impact of sound, we recommend that you look at this part of the book in particular.

According to the Organisation for Economic Co-operation and Development (OECD), we are allocating more and more time to education, increasing the demands placed on learning environments, and at the same time, the opportunities for creating a functioning working environment have never been better.

The book, produced by a working party comprising of members from within and outside Ecophon, will be a source of knowledge and will inspire constructive debate leading to improvements in the learning environment. Few people expect this to happen overnight, but opening your senses to new information is the first small step on the way.

Contents

It is largely through schools and education, whether formal or informal, that culture, traditions and customs are passed on from one generation to the next.

A journey through
the history of education

History has come up with many excellent teachers. Today, reasoning to an informed conclusion is known as the "Socratic method". The Greek philosopher Socrates (469–399 BC) taught through logical, thought-provoking dialogues which sought to awaken opinions. Using questions, Socrates sought to help people understand what was right and good.

This journey through the past demonstrates how ideology and culture have gone hand in hand with developments in education. It also reveals how the power of free speech has changed history.

The past lives on, in us and amongst us, and the way we behave and act is largely determined by our ideological and cultural heritage.

Every society and institution, including the education system, is based on ideological principles. Four forces tend to be emphasised in the formation of social ideologies and institutions:

– **economic**
– **religious**
– **social**
– **political**

The economic factor is considered to play the strongest role. The fundamental needs of people are physical. Closely linked to economic and physical requirements is religion. Irrespective of whether or not one considers that the one is a reflection of the other, people's physical environment is repeated in the religious world. The education system and education have always been influenced by religious power.

"Social" here refers to the organisation and structure of society and interaction between the various parts of the structure. History shows both good and bad structures. One example, is that many older social systems were founded on slavery, which has now been abolished. Class differences have proved to be a characteristic feature of social systems across the world and education has both contributed to and formed these systems.

Different forms of political control have existed since the dawn of time. When ancient tribes grew and were forced to share land with others, new forms of society developed which demanded more advanced management ranging from individual kingdoms to empires, with forms of government varying from despotism to democracy.

From these four forces – economics, religion, social structures and politics – thoughts, attitudes and philosophies have grown up which affect the institutions of society, including the education system.

The preserving power of culture

There is a further force governing social development: culture. It both influences education and depends on it for its survival.

2000 years ago Alexandria was the world's most important centre of knowledge. It was here that great thinkers such as Archimedes and Euclid formed their groundbreaking theories. Over two millennia after the disappearance of the legendary Museion, a new centre of knowledge has been built in the form of the Biblioteca Alexandrina. The main building, with its distinctive circular leaning shape and a diameter of a total 160 metres, houses the main reading room with its 2,500 seats. The style is classical, reminiscent of an Egyptian temple. The building also contains a school, a planetarium, a science centre and a museum.

Culture is possibly the most conservative of all social forces. Cultural values have demonstrated a clear ability to survive unchanged from age to age.

Every society has principles by which it lives, a soul, a culture – something that by its nature is intangible, but which clearly affects the way we behave and act.

Culture can be seen as the summation of a society's spiritual life and reflects human nature and human needs.

Thousands of years ago each tribe had its own culture which distinguished it from other tribes. A person forced to exist outside his or her own tribe was virtually lost. Ideals, emotions, attitudes and convictions – the things that go to make up a culture – have often created greater barriers between people than oceans.

Once the culture is accepted by the group, it provides security but can also hinder new constructive ideas and development. **It is largely through schools and education, whether formal or informal, that culture, traditions and customs are passed on from one generation to the next.**

Change is frightening

The cultural climate changes slowly and at far from the same speed as the material aspects of society. People have always been afraid of change – we are comfortable with the familiar and fear the unknown. People are unwilling to relinquish power and are worried about how access to material resources will be affected. It is likely that this is particularly true of early societies. Way back in the history of mankind knowledge was limited. Phenomena, never experienced before were probably frightening and people would tend to distance themselves from these. Humans have

A practical tool whose roots extend far into the past, the abacus was developed by the ancient world and was originally a board used for counting using small stones. The abacus is still used in China and has proved useful in teaching the visually impaired in the West.

a fundamental need to feel secure, to be assured of the absolute truth, a need which the research and teaching of later eras attempted to fulfil.

Societies and standards developed gradually

In the earliest social systems of the past, **a sense of security was derived from one's own local customs, culture and time-honoured behaviour.**

Over a long period of time an increasingly multi-faceted social life grew – moral standards were developed and social structures and values took on more permanent forms.

Then, as now, geniuses ahead of their time could appear and point the way towards new social structures. Ways of life were also transformed by major crises such as earthquakes, floods and war. Peaceful activities such as trade, also influenced social development.

Changes in surroundings, however, are unable to explain every social revolution. The cause of the fall of some civilisations is still open to speculation even today.

Over time societies became larger. **The major societies which grew up in the Orient offered a new type of security.** Over a long period of time, entire tribes and their cultures merged together. For example, the Chinese Empire, in which tribes comprising of a few hundred families merged to form a great empire, took centuries to develop. These societies also linked people together through customs and culture. As these larger societies were formed, new forms of centralised power were created, controlling politics and education.

Literature a new tool

Another crucial difference between these new societies and the cultures which had gone before was access to literature. This was to contribute to the establishment of an organised education system. It was not until this period, during which the Oriental societies underwent major development, that such a wealth of information could be gathered together.

The past has always been a living and an active force, what takes place in the present draws considerably on what has gone before. People find it difficult even to reason rationally without relating back to experiences from the past. Our laws, customs, morals and institutions are a product of history and this knowledge is primarily passed on through education.

Sub-cultures have held groups of people together throughout history. External attributes such as clothes, hair cuts, etc. have marked people out as members of a particular group since the dawn of time.

Religious literature

During this epoch in human history literature was largely of a religious nature, acting as a unifying social link. Great kingdoms were built on the basis of teachings in Hindu, Persian, Babylonian and Egyptian manuscripts.

The authority of literature was often total. **Documents passed on a society's cultural heritage and other knowledge from generation to generation,** ensuring that in the early Oriental cultures history was ever present.

As in primitive cultures, here too social patterns were formed. During this period, education also acted as a means of passing on opinions and attitudes, often controlled by the church.

The Orient influences the West

Contact, both peaceful and aggressive, gradually increased within the Orient and between the Orient and the Hellenic world (what is now Greece). Influence and ideals from foreign cultures heralded the start of the social revolution which was later to take place in Greece.

During this period the Near East experienced a mixing and reshaping of cultures from various countries. Cretans, Babylonians, Phoenicians, etc. in this region are all the spiritual forefathers of the Greeks and in many ways also of the Westerners of today.

The Greeks discuss new freedoms

At this point in time, a new element was added to the inheritance from the Orient in the form of "freedom" as defined by the ancient Greeks. With historical hindsight, the Oriental peoples seem to have accepted authoritarian rule in a way which gradually came to be entirely alien to the Greeks.

The people of ancient Athens in particular forged a new path characterised by ideas of freedom and originality and **a belief in people's ability to think for themselves and resolve problems** in a changing society. Previously, when it came to solving problems and determining the future direction society was to take, the words, traditions, habits and customs of the church had often repressed individual thought.

People began to question old myths and stories, **knowledge increased, and new academic disciplines saw the light of day.**

However, the results were not always positive, as illustrated by the social unrest and moral collapse which followed the emancipation process in Greece when the yoke of authoritarian, religious and political state power was shed.

Mankind and freedom

Individual freedom was rare in primitive societies, with the exception of particular groups such as successful warriors. In the ancient Orient those wielding political and religious power enjoyed a certain form of freedom. Ancient Greece was the cradle of individual freedom as we know it today, based on freedom of thought. This contributed to new knowledge, new forms of education and modern educational theory, with the opportunity for people to reflect for themselves on what they were told and taught. The ideological revolution which took place in Greece saw the development of society and education take off in a new direction.

Pages 16 – 19 summarise the development of the education and school system from 5000 BC to the modern day.

Today, we are embarking on a new millennium and have knowledge and experience at our disposal that people have gathered throughout history. In addition we have the fantastic resources our highly industrialised society has to offer in the form of advanced technology and opportunities to obtain information via the Internet, radio and television.

What direction will education take in the future? What factors control development?

London's Speaker's Corner can be seen as an expression of our inheritance from the free thinkers of ancient Greece.

Where are we heading?

Important factors for future development include population growth, increasing environmental problems and changes in technology.

Population growth poses two main challenges in the field of education:

- An increasing number of world citizens have to be provided with appropriate education
- Education in family planning is required to ensure that growth does not outstrip resources

The ever increasing destruction of the environment also demands concrete action in terms of education. This must contribute to increased awareness of mankind's ability to survive and develop in a world of limited natural resources.

Changes in technology, on the other hand, both affect the form education takes and offer hope that we will be able to address the population explosion and the destruction of the environment effectively.

Although the earth's resources are still unevenly distributed, it cannot be denied that people in general have gained better material conditions and increased opportunities for education.

New knowledge breeds new insights, new ideas and solutions. The internationalisation we are currently seeing, with the Internet, is taking on increasing importance and means increased exchange of ideas and thoughts at global level, greater dependence on each other irrespective of nationality and, it is hoped, increased co-operation instead of increased opposition.

OECD* facts on education

– Longer time spent in school.

Between 1990 and 1998 the average time a five year-old could look forward to spending sitting at a desk during his or her lifetime increased from 15.1 to 16.4 years. Total time spent in education in OECD countries varies between 12 and 20 years.

– Lifelong learning.

On average, adults participate in adult (further) education for more than the equivalent of a complete academic year during their working life, i.e. between the ages of 25 and 64.

– More people are studying to a high level.

The number of students at universities increased by over 20% between 1990 and 1997 in all but five OECD countries. Eight of the countries saw an increase of over 50%.

– Studying abroad is more common.

The proportion of foreign students at universities choosing to study in an OECD country varies from 1% to approximately 16%.

– Highly educated people are keen to develop their expertise.

Staff with higher qualifications take part in work-related training to a greater extent than staff with lower qualifications. Poor motivation is one of the main reasons why people fail to participate in further training.

– Lack of computers and computer skills.

Lack of access to computer equipment is a major barrier to achieving computing targets in schools. Between 54% and 85% of pupils in the lower years of secondary school suffer this problem.

Having the computer as a tool is increasing distance education. Companies see computer-aided teaching as a solution for skills development.

– Lack of expert computing staff.

An average two out of three students starting secondary education attend schools where the teachers' lack of expertise in computing prevents effective use of computers in their education.

– Education under one's belt makes it easier to find a job.

In general, it is easier to find employment if one has a higher qualification. This difference is greater for women than for men.

What is the point of going to school and learning? One answer might be that the knowledge gained contributes to our achieving self-realisation and enables us to play a part in society.

* Organisation for Economic Cooperation and Development with the task of promoting economic development between the world's leading industrial states.

Cult ceremonies demanded education 5,000 years ago

In ancient Babylon important cult ceremonies meant that education was a prerequisite. Clay tablets showing cuneiform script created by the Sumerians (the earliest known rulers of Babylon) have been found and dated as originating from the 3rd century BC.

The two most powerful pre-oriental cultures of Babylon and Egypt developed complicated pictorial written languages, cuneiform and hieroglyphics respectively.

The alphabet began to be used in around 1200 BC.

The advent of reading and writing led to a need for organised education. Schools were primarily run by temples and palaces, with teaching on school-based lines being found in cultures such as Egypt, India and China. As early as 600 BC members of the higher Indian castes were able to receive up to twelve years of education in various subjects.

Arithmetic became a separate discipline at an early stage and together with writing and reading is one of the world's oldest school subjects. Many other subjects have developed from these three.

The Greeks and schools

The word "school" is derived from the Greek "skhole". It originally meant leisure in the sense of freedom from physical work and employment of the mind.

In Greece, it was primarily the city state of Athens which introduced and inspired permanent forms of schooling and education. Here waxed wooden boards were used as an aid to writing – the first form of slate known to history. The first regulations on compulsory education were issued here in the 6th century BC.

Greek culture and education was passed on throughout the Mediterranean as Greek colonisation spread. A unique centre of knowledge was developed in Alexandria in Egypt, the site of the greatest library of antiquity, *Museion (now being rebuilt in modern guise)*, with a university which can be seen as the first university of the West. Teachers at Museion were paid by the state and many important branches of learning were invented there including geometry, mathematics, astronomy, medicine and linguistics.

The Roman empire

Greek philosophy, literature and art headed the world in the 4th and 5th centuries BC (the classical period). However, the academic and creative power of the Greeks subsequently began to wane.

In conquering Greece, the Roman empire took over many of that civilisation's educational ideas and Greeks were often hired as teachers. Like the Greeks, the Romans set up schools in their colonies, albeit with a more practical focus. Education often took place at home.

The art of discourse was a high priority in the Roman Empire. Roman educator Quintilian wrote a work entitled "Education of an Orator" and was one of the forerunners in looking at upbringing from an early age, demonstrating considerable psycho-logical expertise. Quintilian also addressed the importance of individual teaching and adapting teaching to the ability of the child.

Church and school

After the fall of the Western Roman Empire, Christianity began to spread on a wide front during the medieval period. *Headed by Augustine, one of the fathers of Christianity, a strong organisation was developed in the Catholic church* which demanded first class education and schools. Christian missionary work began in the 6th and 7th centuries *through monastery schools and teaching orders of monks.*

Together with his education minister Alkuin, Charlemagne (742 – 814), King of the Franks and Roman Emperor and a supporter of culture as well as a conqueror, laid the foundations for the progress of the Middle Ages in teaching and research. Charlemagne was interested in public education and the *cathedral schools* in particular enjoyed increased popularity during his reign.

In fulfilment of its responsibility for education, from the 11th century onward the church made the establishment of an effective education system a central feature. From 1073 – 85, all bishops had been asked to see that the art of grammar was taught in their churches.

In the high medieval period Paris was the intellectual centre of Europe, with the University of Paris developing from the cathedral school of Notre Dame. The same period also saw the founding of Cambridge and Oxford universities.

WINTER TRAINING AREA (COVERED) FOR ATHLETES

ARENA

HOT BATHS

TEMPERATE ROOM

LACONICUM (SWEAT ROOM)

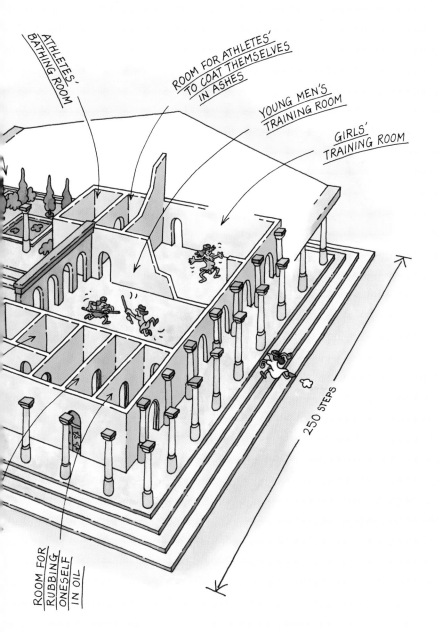

ATHLETES' BATHING ROOM

ROOM FOR ATHLETES' TO COAT THEMSELVES IN ASHES

YOUNG MEN'S TRAINING ROOM

GIRLS' TRAINING ROOM

250 STEPS

ROOM FOR RUBBING ONESELF IN OIL

The palaestras and porticos* of the Greeks

"… of the buildings created by the ancient Greeks, where the men went to train their bodies, it is very likely that at that time when the cities of Greece were republics, that in every city there was such a building, where the young men, as well as gaining book learning, trained in the arts of combat, such as moving in serried ranks, throwing the lance, wrestling, handling weapons and swimming with a heavy load on their shoulders so as to become able to meet the challenges and dangers of war."

"Firstly a square area was staked out, and on three of the sides simple colonnades were built and entering from these some spacious rooms where learned men, philosophers and similar sat in talk and discussion. On the fourth side, which faced south, a double colonnade was built which prevented the wind blowing the rain in during the winter and in the summer kept the sun off as much as possible. In the centre of this colonnade was a very large room, twice as long as it was wide, and in this the young men trained. To the right of this lay the girls' training room and behind it the room in which the athletes covered themselves in ashes; further away in the corner was the cold bath room. To the left of the young men's training room was the changing room and further round, the warm room which was heated and opened onto the hot room. The latter had the laconicum on one side (where people sweated) and on the other the room for warm bathing."

(Source: Andrea Palladio, Four books on architecture, 1570/1983)
* Palaestra = Arena, Portico = Columned Hall

Oxford, the first university in England, dates from the 12th–13th century when Henry II ordered the English students on the continent to return to England. Many of these students decided to settle in Oxford in an attempt to create the kind of university they had seen in Europe, however, disputes between the students and the residents led to riots. The first students arrived in Cambridge in 1209 after fleeing from the rioting in Oxford to establish a new university.

Public education

During the 16th century the authority of the church began to be questioned, while technology developed fast. *Gutenberg and his new art of printing* boosted teaching and culture. Protestant reformer Martin Luther's Small Catechism was disseminated as a textbook and the idea of public education gained a greater foothold. The counter-reformation of the Catholic church, intended to stem the progress of Protestantism, led to new educational opportunities in the form of the Jesuit schools. These were outstanding in methodology and were also interested in teacher training.

In England, during the 16th century, the separation of the Church of England from the Church of Rome, under Henry VIII, did not have the same repercussions in the education field that were experienced by the continental Reformations. The secondary school system had been strongly influenced by the Renaissance before the reforms and many grammar schools were already established. The situation,

however, became precarious for political reasons due a succession of sovereigns. Henry VIII included the schools in his policy of concentration and consolidation of power in the hands of the state. In 1548, Edward VI passed the Charities Act, which confiscated the church estates expressly for use in education. However both Edward VI, and then his sister Mary I, allowed the funds allocated to education to be diverted elsewhere – meaning many grammar schools disappeared due to lack of funds. However in 1558, Elizabeth I revived Henry VIII's educational policy and more money was allocated to education.

Universities go from strength to strength

In Great Britain the need for education increased. By the end of the 15th century Scotland had three universities – St Andrews, Glasgow and Aberdeen. Edinburgh followed in 1582. The founding of universities was naturally accompanied by an increase in schools of many kinds. In most parts of Western Europe, including England and Wales, there were soon grammar schools, of some type, available for boys. It was estimated by the close of the Middle Ages, that with a population of about 2.5 million, there were approximately 400 grammar

schools, from which later emerged public schools. Throughout the 17th century public education in Great Britain improved.

Galileo was active at the start of the 17th century and Newton towards its end, while Francis Bacon and others formed the basis of a new philosophy, inductive reasoning, which involved empirical deduction based on a series of observations. The 1650s saw the advent of Johan Amos Comenius, in what was then the Austrian Empire, whose school programme and methodological ideas gained great popularity and are also reflected in teaching today. Comenius thought that teaching should be graphic, ideally based on objects themselves and adapted to the age of the pupil. In England from the 17th century onwards, educational establishments were founded by rival Christian sects, while at a village level simple instruction was on offer in the so-called "Dame Schools" – where local women taught children for a small fee.

In the 16th and 17th centuries, scholistic programmes reflected changes in society in both England and Scotland. Importance was given

to English, science, modern languages and sport, as is the case today, through the National Curriculum.

The first teacher training colleges, worthy of the name, were established in the 18th century in Germany. 1760 saw the publication of Jean-Jaques Rousseau's literary work "Emile", which advocated human goodness and came to revolutionise attitudes to bringing up children.

Compulsory education in the UK

The 19th century was characterised by the industrial revolution which, in England, influenced the development of a "national" education. In England, the monitorial system of education was developed (the Lancaster method) where teachers and bright pupils taught huge numbers of children, up to a couple of hundred at a time.

New discoveries in science encouraged secularisation and the separation of church and state. Charles Darwin's theory of evolution became generally accepted.

In England during the 19th century the state began to accept responsibility for the nation's education, with the Elementary Education Act in 1870. *In 1880, an education act was passed which made education in England and* Wales compulsory. *In Scotland, it was a little earlier with education being made compulsory in 1872.* The 1891 Education Act established that state schools must be entirely free of even subsidiary charges. The 1944 Education Act extended the principle of free compulsory schooling to include secondary education, thus raising the school leaving age to 15.

The educational systems of Scotland

Under the Lancaster method teaching was largely carried out by brighter children, monitors. The teacher circulated the room and intervened where necessary. The telegraph at one end of the bench signalled when the group had finished its task. The day began with hymn singing and prayers, with the teacher playing the psalmodikon, a stringed instrument. Illustration from Helsingborg School Museum, Sweden.

A school classroom of the early 1900s.

and Northern Ireland are separate from that of England and Wales. The Education Act of 1944 of England and Wales was reproduced for both Scotland and Northern Ireland in 1945 and 1947, respectively, to include adaptations required through local traditions and environment.

The start of the 20th century was heralded by great optimism for the future. This was soon blighted by increasing social unrest and the First World War. Swedish writer Ellen Key achieved international acclaim for her book "The Century of the Child" (1900), which describes a strong belief in development in upbringing and teaching.

New psychology and educational theories

During this period science gained increased influence compared with the teachings of the church, which were based on theology and metaphysics. America firmly entered the educational debate at the turn of the century, a leading figure being John Dewey, known as the father of progressive pedagogy, who launched the concept of "learning by doing". America also came to dominate the debate on the psychology of learning.

Movements in psychology and educational theory include:

• Russian reflexology based on Ivan Pavlov's theory of the conditional reflex

• Behaviourism – the effect of learned behaviour on human actions

THE CHILD

What will he become?

School   Literary Institution   Profession and Marriage   Honoured Age

The Street   Beer-shop   Vice and Misery   Beggary

In olden days expectations were made as to how a child would develop. Schooling was crucial to one's future as an adult. Illustration from Cassell's Illustrated Family Paper, 1862.

• Maria Montessori's ideas about independent child rearing

• Gestalt psychology, which sees representations and mental processes as wholes

• International comparative educational theory, in which countries learn from each others' education systems and gain a perspective on their own

Why do we want to learn things? One psychological explanation comes from American Jerome Bruner, who considers that humans have three intrinsic motives:

- *Curiosity, we are investigative by nature.*

- *Expertise, we want to achieve expertise in relation to our surroundings.*

- *Mutuality, we inherently seek to work with others to achieve common goals.*

Points to remember:

- Ideologies and social institutions and education systems were formed from economic, religious, social and political factors.

- Culture can be seen as the summation of a society's spiritual life and is passed on through education.

- Free, democratic thinking gained a breakthrough in Ancient Greece.

- Environmental issues, population growth and the development of technology are some of the factors guiding the education of the future.

- The global exchange of ideas will increase in the future, partly because of the Internet.

- The word "school" comes from the Greek "skhole" and originally meant leisure in the sense of freedom from physical work and employment of the mind.

- Alexandria was the site of the first Western university.

- Orders of monks, and monastery and cathedral schools were early seats of learning.

- England gained a national curriculum around the 16th and 17th centuries.

- Compulsory education was introduced in England and Wales in 1880 and in Scotland in 1872.

- Education helps us to achieve self-realisation and prepares us and enables us to play a part in society.

- The time spent in education is increasing in OECD countries.

References – A journey through the history of education

Börjesson, Lena (1992). *ABC-bok om lärande (ABC of learning)*. Metoda. (in Swedish)

Encyclopædia Britannica

Gage, N. L. & Berliner, David C. (1998). *Educational psychology*. Houghton Mifflin. (in English)

Maltén, Arne (1999). *Vad är kunskap? (What is knowledge?)* Gleerups Förlag. (in Swedish)

Mulhern, James (1959). *A history of education: a social interpretation*. The Ronald Press Company. (in English)

OECD (Organisation for Economic Co-operation and Development)/Centre for Educational Research and Innovation Indicators of Education Systems (2000). *Education at a glance: OECD indicators*. OECD. (in English)

Palladio, Andrea (1570/1983). *Fyra böcker om arkitekturen (Four books on architecture)*. Vinga Bokförlag. (original 1570, this edition 1983) (original in Italian, in Swedish)

Pedersen, Odd & Svantesson, Bo (1976). *Undervisningsteknologi: Utbildningsplanering och samhälle (Educational techniques: Planning education and society)*. LiberLäromedel. (in Swedish)

Sandström, Carl Ivar (1989). *Utbildningens idéhistoria (The history of ideas of education)*. Svensk Facklitteratur. (in Swedish)

Steinberg, John M. (1998). *Låt skolan dö – länge leve lärandet! (The Death of Schooling – Long Live Learning!)* Ekelund. (in Swedish)

Thomas, Robert Murray (ed.) (1990). *International comparative education: practices, issues and prospects*. Pergamon Press. (in English)

A good working environment and a functioning indoor environment are one of the best possible investments.

Learning requires a holistic approach to the indoor environment

The indoor environment of schools and other educational facilities must help ensure that students and staff feel both mentally and physically healthy.

People who feel well can study, teach and complete other tasks more effectively.

Many of us remember boring afternoon lessons, during which indoor air quality had deteriorated and the burning sun had heated up the classroom considerably. Neither teachers nor students perform at their best in such conditions.

A study carried out into links between room temperature and mental activity in schools has shown that when the temperature reaches 30°C, performance drops to around 80% of the performance measured at 22°C.

One way of compensating for higher temperatures is to increase sound levels to help maintain the same level of alertness, but this method should be avoided, as sound levels are already high in schools.

Sound, climate, air quality, working position, light and lighting are key areas of the indoor environment highlighted in this chapter. Other areas addressed include the factors which help to form the perception of the room and environmental considerations in schools.

The sound section complements other parts of **"Don't Limit Your Senses"** which discuss the impact of sound.

A holistic approach is vital to achieve a functional and healthy physical environment. The battle is almost won from the start if such an approach is possible early in the building process. Therefore, this chapter also has a section on this process and ways of influencing it.

Sounds which have an impact

*The teacher plays a key role in teaching, as does
the acoustic environment.*

How useful is a good teacher who can't be heard properly?
*This section takes a brief look at the significance of sound
in an indoor environment. For more detailed information,
see the chapters "Sound in the learning environment" and
"Advice on room acoustics in educational premises".*

Many of today's teaching premises have an acoustic environment which
hampers education. It is often difficult to hear everything which is said
and various types of noise are extremely irritating. Successful education
is not just about having a good teacher, the way room acoustics and noise
are handled is also crucial.

Noise and poor room acoustics can be remedied

Speech intelligibility and thus learning, are reduced by various kinds of
noise, such as the hum of ventilation, speech, traffic noise, the scraping
of chairs and footsteps. Sound from adjoining areas is another source
of noise. Disturbing sound spreads to other parts of the building from
gymnasiums, workshops and music rooms in particular, as well as
corridors, stairs, lifts and ventilation units. The effects can be reduced,
by having separate or structurally divided premises and sound insulated
doors with a good seal. Footsteps are also a major noise problem in
schools, to the extent that some become "shoe free" by deciding to ban
outdoor shoes indoors.

Noise has a particular impact on tasks that require a great deal of thinking and concentration and those which involve memory and multi-tasking. In addition, the noise can be irritating.

A common form of noise is the low-frequency, monotonous and tiring sound from ventilation. Therefore, ventilation and air-conditioning units should be checked and adjusted as necessary to reduce the sound level, possibly by adding sound dampers or quieter blower units. Disturbing noise is particularly noticeable when heating and cooling systems are switched on and off during the working day.

External background noise, such as traffic noise, can be reduced using windows with double (triple etc.) glazing, which also help provide a more even indoor temperature. A simple and cheap way of combating this type of noise is to replace worn-out window seals with new, effective ones.

Noise created in areas where people congregate can be efficiently dampened using full acoustic ceilings which reduce sound propagation and improve speech intelligibility. The cost of an acoustic ceiling is no more than that of plastering and painting the existing ceiling.

The next chapter "Sound in the learning environment" will go into more depth on the subject of room acoustics and the impact of noise on education and people's wellbeing.

"Good acoustics is central to classroom learning and is therefore vital to every knowledge-based society... Poor acoustics is the single most common environmental complaint affecting many millions of children in the US."

(Picard and Bradley. USA, 1997)

"The acoustic conditions in the majority of classrooms studied were unacceptable."

(50 schools with 106 classrooms and 149 teachers were involved in the study which focused on Year 1 pupils. Blake and Busby. New Zealand, 1994)

Climate and air quality

Thermal climate, air quality and ventilation are factors that, to a large extent, affect our ability to carry out a full day's work at our best. Warm classrooms can create negative stress.

The right indoor temperature and good air quality improves performance. The temperature should be 20°C or just over in the classroom and should be evenly distributed around the whole room, including areas next to the windows. This means using appropriate heating to avoid cold rooms in the winter, while during warm periods, direct sunlight must be avoided, by using blinds for example. Double (triple etc.) glazing and fully sealed window frames help maintain an even temperature and a draught-free indoor environment. This also provides better sound insulation against noise from outside and more efficient energy use.

Warm rooms with a temperature significantly higher than 20°C can lead to negative stress and the increased production of the stress hormone cortisol. Heat can also make it difficult to maintain concentration and stay awake.

There appears to be a link between the indoor environment and health, but there is still some uncertainty about exactly which factors cause the symptoms (For example mucous membrane problems, headaches and rashes). The known contributory factors include poor ventilation, hazardous emissions from building materials and damp and mould problems.

Keep carbon dioxide in check

As the air indoors is polluted by our breathing (rising carbon dioxide levels), we increasingly become tired, get headaches and find it difficult to concentrate. **Carbon dioxide levels should not exceed 1,000 ppm (parts per million),** but the figure rises quickly in poorly ventilated rooms, often up to 3,000 ppm or more, with high carbon dioxide levels affecting those within the rooms. Naturally, having to hold lessons in such an environment is undesirable. It is not enough to air the room before lessons, but rather an efficient, constant flow of fresh air is required.

Getting the right air quality and thermal climate

Air and thermal climate requirements can, to a certain extent, be met by having spacious rooms (although not good for room acoustics) and a heavy floor structure which, combined with thick walls, can absorb outdoor heat or cold overnight and so even out the temperature indoors throughout the day. Mechanical ventilation and air conditioning units can be costly solutions in terms of energy, but they **are often necessary in teaching premises where the temperature and air quality need to be kept at a relatively constant level.** In certain cases an acceptable flow of air can be created through the natural draught principle based on thermology (warm air rises) using openable dampers and windows. There are numerous solutions and these are just a few ways of creating the right thermal climate, air quality and ventilation.

Allergies – a major problem

Certain countries have very high numbers of children with allergies or other hypersensitivity, with sensitivity to pollen and animal fur particularly common. Avoiding carpets and other textiles which collect dust and allergens is a good way of reducing the risk. It is sometimes necessary for classrooms to be fully adapted for allergy sufferers by choosing building materials and furniture that do not emit hazardous substances and by carefully avoiding textiles which can adversely affect health. **A guide is to choose environmentally approved building materials.**

A common problem in the working environment is a feeling of dryness of the eyes, skin and upper airways. The fact that staff and students perceive the air to be too dry does not necessarily mean that it actually is. This feeling of dryness may be due to dust and other particles, too high an indoor temperature or chemical substances from building materials,

A dirty rug caused productivity to drop 6% in a Danish study.

paints, carpets, etc. Preventing the spread of dust and allergens requires repeated inspection of the ventilation and air-conditioning units. Ventilation ducts and filters must be thoroughly cleaned. Careful, regular and, as far as possible, chemical-free cleaning of rooms considerably improves conditions for allergy sufferers and other hypersensitive people.

At the Danish Technological Institute, researchers have studied the way people react to the source of pollution indoors. An item as trivial as a very dirty rug was hidden in the areas where the test group worked. The number of people who complained about the poor indoor environment or other problems increased and people, who from the beginning considered themselves sensitive to problems with the indoor environment, felt that the air was dryer. At the same time productivity dropped by 6%.

Working position and strain injuries

It is not just poor working positions which strain the body. Noise too can cause strain injuries.

The working position for students and teachers has to be comfortable for education to be effective.

Physical tension caused by poor working positions can lead to joint and muscle pain. Stress factors such as noise, poor lighting, time pressure and unhappiness can also cause strain injuries when the body has had enough and lets you know it.

Good ergonomics

Poor working positions can cause symptoms such as headaches, back pain, shoulder pain, neck pain and tiredness.

A study which looked at school children in later life showed that students who suffered aching neck and shoulder muscles at the age of 16 had similar problems ten years later.

Ergonomically designed, height-adjustable chairs and tables reduce the risk of strain injuries. In particular, desks which are too low encourage pupils to bend over the tabletop in what is an abnormal position for the body.

Other working environment factors also create stressful muscle tension, e.g. when you have to strain to hear, or to avoid glare, as there is a risk of twisting the body into an unnatural position.

The increase in v.d.u. (monitor) work in educational establishments places special demands on ergonomics with regard to movement patterns, working positions, lighting and noise from the computers.

Relaxation exercises can be used to reduce the risk of strain problems and these also increase the ability to concentrate and improve sleep patterns. Muscle and stretching exercises can also make the body more adept at dealing with stresses and strains.

Energy yawns are carried out by massaging the muscles around the joint between the temple and the jaw. This can be found just in front of the ear and is the joint where the lower jaw meets the upper jaw. Over this joint run five major skull nerves which receive sensory information from the whole face, the eye muscles, the tongue and the mouth and activate all the facial, eye and mouth muscles. When we are stressed, we often tense our jaw, reducing the nerve function in this area. Energy yawning allows the whole facial area to relax, making it easier to appreciate sensations and also to communicate.

(From the book "Smart Moves". C Hannaford. Great Ocean Publishers, 1998)

Don't Limit Your Senses Learning requires a holistic approach to the indoor environment

Light and lighting

Daylight should always be used as much as possible. When planning educational premises, look first at letting in daylight and then complement this with good artificial lighting.

Light has a major impact on the way we perceive a room. The brightness and shadows formed by the daylight penetrating Grand Central Station in New York, built in 1936, create a grand and mystical atmosphere which would otherwise not exist in our senses. The appropriate light, in the right place, is vital to the work carried out in a room.

The characteristics of the lighting are crucial to our happiness, wellbeing and work. Light, or lack of light, can make us exhilarated or depressed, it can stimulate us or make us tired. **The lighting in a workplace must also satisfy the sight requirements for the work in question.** Sufficient, good quality light means:

- Glare-free light
- Light in the right direction
- Appropriate shadow formation
- Adaptable for sight impairment, e.g. in older people
- Good colour rendering through appropriate light colour and absence of flickering
- A harmonious perception of the room through well-lit surfaces and even light distribution

Make the most of light

Many rooms have fixed light fittings in the ceiling, most of which direct light downwards and fail to provide sufficiently even light levels within the room. The aim should be to achieve **sufficient even lighting throughout the room** so that everyone can enjoy the same opportunity to see well. The best way to achieve this is by using **uplighters, lighting which provides indirect light via the ceiling**. Using the ceiling as a reflector creates soft, diffused light which spreads throughout the room and reduces the risk of irritating glare. The ceiling must be a light colour and have high reflectivity, with the surface being able to spread light in every direction (diffusion). Light walls, in particular, increase the effect of light reflection.

It is not enough for the ceiling to be light to function as an effective light reflector. To achieve maximum effect from indirect lighting, the ceiling must provide high light reflection and diffusion (the surface's ability to spread light in different directions in the room).

The right lights in the right place

The choice of luminaire (light fitting) does not only have to do with the light requirements within a room. Often, luminaires have to meet fire safety requirements in certain environments, such as woodworking workshops, or be able to tolerate dampness in wet rooms and meet requirements for electrical safety. The lighting in gymnasium ceilings must be adapted to provide sufficient light right down to floor-level, and sometimes luminaires need to be able to withstand hard knocks. In classrooms and offices uplighters are usually ideal for achieving the best possible light.

To create aesthetic effects in rooms, combine different types of lighting making use of indirect and direct light, ceiling and wall lights, etc.

The lighting has to meet the needs of those whose sight is worst. Bear in mind the fact that many older teachers and students need more light to see well. A 60-year old may need up to seven times more light than a 10-year old. Increasing light reflection can significantly increase the strength of a room's lighting.

To achieve particular effects using indirect light, for example in an entrance, assembly hall or canteen, build a light coffer housing indirect lighting.

Choose the right light to avoid glare

Increased risk of glare occurs where there are major luminance differences (differences in brightness) between the illuminating area of the luminaire and other surfaces in the room, such as the ceiling. Think how much stronger the glare from the headlights of an oncoming car feels at night, compared with car headlights in daylight. When it is dark, the difference in luminance between the beam of the headlights and the surroundings is much greater than it is in daylight. A similar effect can occur in a room, so it is advisable to consider carefully which type of lighting provides the least amount of glare.

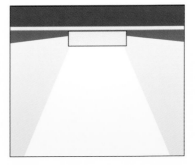

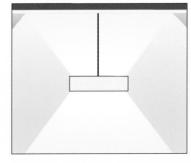

Recessed downlighters often require a highly effective anti-glare shield. Even so, there is always a major difference in luminance between the light source and the ceiling, which significantly increases the risk of glare.

Surface-mounted downlighters often require a highly effective anti-glare shield. Even so, there is always a major difference in luminance between the light source and the ceiling, which significantly increases the risk of glare. If light is also spread from the vertical parts of the light fitting, these may also cause glare.

Some suspended downlighters are designed to cast a certain amount of light upwards onto the ceiling, making the difference in luminance somewhat less compared with the previous lighting solutions. However, the majority of the light is cast downwards and may cause glare without an effective anti-glare shield.

Suspended uplighters mainly illuminate the ceiling, which reflects light across the whole room. Effective indirect light requires a ceiling with high reflectivity and diffusion, a broad spectrum of light and a highly efficient luminaire (efficiency in terms of the ratio of light emitted from the luminaire to light from the light source, e.g. the fluorescent tube). This solution provides the smallest difference in luminance between the luminaire and the ceiling, which drastically reduces the risk of glare. However, a small amount of light should be directed downwards to achieve a certain amount of shadowing around work areas, as this makes it easier to judge distances.

Possibly the only time glare is considered positive is when the sun glitters romantically on the sea. But in the long run even this is tiring and distracting, not least when out sailing.

Glare – the biggest lighting problem in the workplace

Glare involves a reaction to major light sources in a person's field of vision. **The phenomenon can make it more difficult to see and make people feel uncomfortable and tired.** This is because the eye has major problems constantly adapting to different light conditions.

The main principle is to have even light levels over the whole area without people being disturbed by glaring light sources. Glare should be avoided directly in the line of sight, for example from poorly shielded luminaires and windows. Even if there is no direct sunlight coming through the window, the sky may be perceived as glaring if the field of vision is directed towards the window. In order to eliminate glare, the workplace should be free from shiny materials which cause disturbing flashes.

Glare may also cause physical effects relating to the working environment, such as eye strain, headaches and strain injuries, as people unconsciously twist their bodies into unnatural positions to avoid disturbing flashes of light. Typical symptoms include pains in the back and the neck.

Choose the right colour temperature and avoid flicker and noise

Good colour vision depends on a well thought-out choice of light source with the right colour rendering (the light source's ability to reproduce colours as accurately as possible).

Tubular fluorescent lamps are the most common light source in schools. Heat radiation is low and there is a choice of three light colours: warm white, white and daylight. It is important that the light source reproduces as many colours as possible and that the light feels natural. Full-colour tubes with good colour rendering are recommended.

Fluorescent lights should be fitted with an electronic ballast (HF ballast) to **achieve flicker-free light.** The electronic ballast avoids the low-frequency humming which may occur with an electromagnetic ballast and which may be spread via vibrations in the light fitting.

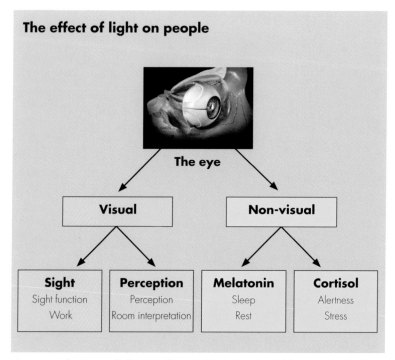

The eye performs a sight function, for example in work and perception (visual tasks) as well as a wakefulness and sleep function (non-visual effects). Based on the model by researcher Roger Wibom of the Swedish National Institute for Working Life.

Light – not just for sight

Light not only affects the ability to see, it also contributes to making us feel awake and alert or tired and depressed. Lack of light affects the pineal gland's production of the sleep hormone melatonin. Production is high in low light, but many people are also affected during the day at dark times of the year, when increased sleep hormone production fools the body into thinking it is time to sleep. Many people get tired and others suffer recurring seasonal depression.

It is crucial to wellbeing that the entire room has plenty of light and not just the work areas. Indirect light is an effective solution for lighting the room's surfaces and so creating good light conditions in the whole room.

A study by Rickard Küller, Professor of Environmental Psychology at Lund University in Sweden, shows that people in Northern Europe, in this case Sweden and the UK, feel worse during the dark months of the year than people in Saudia Arabia, for example, where the amount of light remains more or less the same throughout the year. People do not experience the same seasonal changes in mental health there. According to the study, when daylight returns to Northern Europe, many people feel better than they did during the dark winter months.

A lot of light increases production of the hormone cortisol, which has a major impact on our alertness. However, having too high a cortisol level can cause increased stress.

Daylight, valuable but difficult to control

In contrast to artificial light, daylight cannot be controlled, **it varies in strength and colour depending on time of day and the weather.** Despite this, architects strive to utilise daylight as much as possible; it is a free source of light to complement and replace artificial light. In addition, architects can use the influx of daylight to give shape to buildings and rooms by using shadow effects, contrasts, etc. Natural light is the preferred choice for human eyes and wellbeing. However, it is not always enough, which is why it has to be supplemented by artificial light. Today's light sources, fittings and opportunities to spread light via ceilings with high reflectivity and diffusion make artificial light an effective and necessary complement to daylight – if you plan your lighting correctly.

Perception of a room

Students and staff feel better and work more efficiently in a healthy, functional and stimulating learning environment.
 What should you think about when it comes to choosing colour, design and materials? Here are some tips and advice.

Our emotions and ability to learn are affected to a large extent by what we see around us. A building is a source of experience in which people's work, communication, social interaction and wellbeing are affected by the design of the whole as well as the individual room and furnishings.

Well thought-out architecture and well-planned colour schemes and design language are the cornerstones on which a pleasant workplace is built.

Therefore, it is worth taking a holistic approach from the start when addressing factors which affect emotional impressions in an educational environment. As well as sound, light, air and other indoor environmental factors, these also include colour, design of rooms and furnishings, choice of surface finish, etc.

A room gains its shape and visual qualities from the co-ordination of materials, colour, design, proportions and the light characteristics from daylight or electric light.

A clear design language and architecture make it easier not to get lost. This is a priority in all environments and buildings but particularly in educational establishments where people move between different parts of the building. A more personal and perhaps surprising design can give a room an individual and exciting character, although it may not be

as easy to take in. In general it is a matter of achieving a balance between a clearly logical/functional architectural approach and unexpected ideas to provide inspiration.

A room is not just four walls, a floor and a ceiling. The room as we perceive it is made up of boundaries both physical and derived from light, sound and views to adjacent environments, for example through windows.

From a psychological point of view, it is important that those who spend time in and work in a room clearly perceive its boundaries in the form of visible differences between floor, ceiling and walls. **A feeling of being in a delimited room creates security and feeling secure is vital for successful learning.** A room too large for its function can feel empty and exposed. It can also be seen as muddled, as its boundary surfaces are difficult to perceive, alternatively a small room can easily feel cramped and enclosed. Creating the right sized room is a vital issue but it is not always easy to achieve. What do you do when class sizes change? What solutions are the most appropriate when rooms have to accommodate large and small groups? How large should assembly rooms be? What should the boundaries between rooms look like?

Daylight and lighting

Daylight and lighting are key elements of the design of a room, varying light can enable the same physical space to take on different forms. Light and dark strongly affect the perception of a room. For example, light rooms are seen as larger than dark ones. For more on the impact of light, see page 37.

Colour environment, happiness and study efficiency

Perceptions of colour can be emotional or purely objective observations.

Emotional perceptions of colour may mean that colours are felt to be warm or cold, beautiful or ugly, calming or exciting, etc., depending on the person viewing them. Colours can also have a symbolic value. Symbolism often has cultural roots, with the meaning of a colour differing from culture to culture.

Colour choice, lightness, darkness, colour strength and contrasts can even be used to achieve diametrically opposed effects such as calm or chaos, hot or cold, cosy homeliness or the perception of an institutional environment.

This has a major impact on our ability to concentrate. **An emotionally calming colour in the classroom helps pupils to concentrate more easily, which results in more effective learning.** Adding small splashes of colours which increase alertness can achieve a balanced colour scheme which primarily calms but also has a sufficiently energising effect.

The colour scheme is intimately bound up with the room design. Colour can help strengthen, or tone down, architectual effects.

When the architect uses colour to accentuate his or her architectual composition, great new opportunities open up.

Colour is a major factor in creating a conscious feeling for a room, as here in this main hall and in this canteen at a Swedish school.

Creating order with colour

Colours can also be used to strengthen the relationship between different rooms.

A well thought-out colour scheme not only builds up the atmosphere, it can also create **logic and order,** and make it easier for people to orient themselves in a building or a room.

Choice of colour also affects the **lightness** of a room. As incoming daylight and artificial light must be able to be reflected off walls, floor and ceiling, light colours are often the best choice. If you want to add colour to a room, without having too great an impact on light reflection, one option is to paint only the back wall. A strong colour on just one wall is often enough to give character to the whole room, even if the other surfaces are light-coloured.

In a canteen, warm tones, along with a wide variety of lighting, can create a relaxing environment, however, in a classroom attention and concentration are required, which choice of colour can help to create. It is worth remembering not to use highly expressive colours, as they can create undesirable emotional effects such as anxiety and stress.

The choice of surface material also has a major impact on the perception of a room and the colour environment. Natural materials such as wood or stone floors and tiled walls feel welcoming to many people and are considered appropriate in entrances, for example. From the point of view of light, the materials should have light colours and important reflecting surfaces such as ceilings should be white to optimise the light.

Schools and other learning environments are often organised into departments. The aim is to keep together groups of pupils and offer things on a smaller scale, creating a feeling of community, security and responsibility. Each department can be given an identity through its own colour scheme and design language which links areas together visually and strengthens the feeling of belonging among pupils and staff.

Children feel worse in muddled environments

A uniform and ordered environment has a major impact on children's behaviour. Disruptive children in particular function worse in a muddled physical environment.

Environmental psychologist Thorbjörn Laike of Lund Institute of Technology in Sweden has carried out a study at nine Swedish daycare centres. Reactions to various colour schemes and design languages were studied in 78 children between the ages of three and seven. The study looked at changes in the children's levels of activity as well as their emotional behaviour.

The daycare centre's physical environment was shown to have a major impact on the children's emotions and behaviour. A room with muddled furnishings and strong and varied colours complicates the situation and children lose the context. Colours on furniture and textiles, noticeboards and decorations also have a major impact on the way people perceive the room. This particularly affects children with

Colour in a classroom changes the perception of the room. The colour of the beams affects the whole room without having any major impact on the function of the light-reflecting surfaces.

In buildings, colour is never perceived as a separate element – we are affected by its interplay with materials and shapes.

concentration problems and disruptive children, as they become more hyperactive. The behaviour was also verified in the study as an increased level of activity on an ECG.

According to the survey, different colours have different effects, such as red, which has a stressful effect whilst blue appears more calming.

A more important factor is the strength of the colour in the room. Pale tones are usually a better choice than strong ones. Stronger colours can be used as accents in an otherwise calm and balanced colour environment.

The most important factor of all is well thought-out fittings, as form and colour together create an ordered environment. This increases contentment and has a calming effect, particularly on disruptive children.

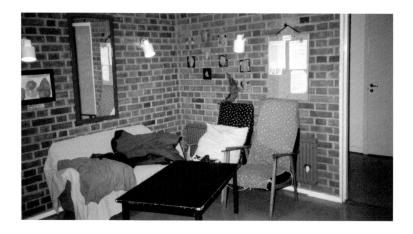

Interiors from two daycare centres studied with regard to the children's emotional reactions and behaviour. The environment above made many children uneasy and hyperactive, while the room below had a calming effect.

The building process and the environment

Understanding the building process and knowing who the key parties are helps in getting involved and having a say in the design of learning environments.

This section also looks at the importance of setting environmental goals and presents a number of principles to bear in mind when discussing an environmental programme.

The building process comprises of the activities required to plan, implement and follow-up a building project, be it a newbuild or refurbishment, rather than simply the actual construction. The building process involves a number of parties:

The **users** (pupils/students and staff) utilise the physical environment. They are directly affected by any faults and deficiencies which the building may have, but also enjoy the fruits of good building design.

Regulatory bodies lay down standards and regulations which will help provide good environments in our society.

The **client** is responsible for the building, and will enter into a contract with the construction company to carry out the work.

The **designers**, e.g. the architects, engineers, acoustics experts or other specialists, are consultants who plan, design and bring specialist skills to the shape and function of the building. The designers interpret the requirements placed on the building by the client.

The **building contractor** (construction company) constructs the building.

The **suppliers** supply materials, knowledge and expertise.

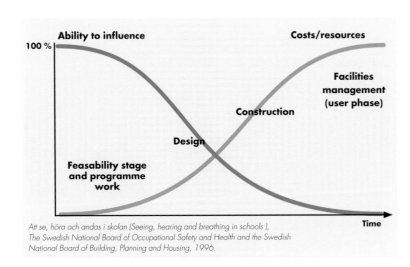

Att se, höra och andas i skolan (Seeing, hearing and breathing in schools),
The Swedish National Board of Occupational Safety and Health and the Swedish
National Board of Building, Planning and Housing, 1996.

The **facilities managers** make the physical environment available to the users and maintain this environment throughout its life.

The **project manager,** is the building project's "managing director" and is the person appointed by the client to co-ordinate the project activities. It used to be common for architects to perform this function, but many countries now have specialist consultants who take on this responsibility. The project manager's position in the organisation and authority vary according to the type of contract.

The main activities of the building process

The main activities of the building process are the **feasability stage, programme work** (project planning), **design, contract procurement and tendering, construction** (production) and **facilities management** (user phase).

Contract procurement – tendering and signing/sealing contracts – may take place at various times depending on the type of contract.

In addition to the requirements of the user, the building process is also affected by political decisions, local planners, standards and environmental measures. Resources such as land, funding, planning issues, building products and labour as well as location and climate are other contributory factors.

The ability to achieve value for money is the major factor in the early stages of the building process. It is therefore vital that the staff involved, the users (the customers of the educational establishment) and the facilities manager receive information as early as possible and are allowed to express their opinions and experience. Measures brought in at a late stage can be very costly.

In order to achieve an optimum environment it is important to let all interested parties take part in the building process at an early stage:

- *Those having the building built*

- *Those planning and designing the building*

- *Those doing the construction work*

- *Those responsible for the daily operation of the building*

- *Other experts (e.g. in areas such as the environment, acoustics, lighting, ventilation)*

- *Those who will be using the building (e.g. students, teachers, staff and possibly parents)*

Set environmental and quality targets from the start

In the initial feasability stage appropriate requirements are set according to a programme which takes into account life cycle and future maintenance. This is the point at which targets for external environmental impact and the indoor and working environment are set. Here are a few examples:

- Plan educational premises in quiet surroundings. Avoid building near major roads, airports, industrial areas, etc. As this may not be possible, external environmental conditions should be taken into accout in the design.

- Do not build on damp or otherwise unsuitable land. Again, if this is unavoidable, allow additional funds to treat adverse ground conditions. Ensure that the foundations have time to dry out properly.

- Resource management, energy efficiency and life cycle adaptations are key words to bear in mind when choosing a design, building materials and installations. Make the most of your resources to achieve a good learning environment.

- Naturally, the most important factor is the building's ability to meet demands relating to education and learning and to contribute to good health and general wellbeing.

Principles to bear in mind in discussions on an environmental programme

During the programme work stage (project planning), an environmental programme should be created based on the requirements, principles and goals. The environmental programme should conclude with a document aimed at ensuring that the building's functions will promote a good indoor and external environment. This will then form the basis for a project-specific environmental plan, a practical tool in planning, material purchasing and construction. Consideration should also be given to the way requirements can be met for minimum maintenance and efficient operation.

- Working environment functions (room planning, air and climate, sound impact, room acoustics, lighting, etc.)

- The characteristics of building materials in an indoor environment, plus design and system choices (chemical constituents, damp properties, "quiet" installations, environmental certification, etc.)

- Exterior environmental characteristics (sustainable, low-maintenance building materials taking into account life cycle, designs and systems for energy-efficient operation, environmental certification, etc.)

1. Overall environmental targets

Decide on the quality level by formulating overall environmental targets for the construction project, whether it involves a newbuild, refurbishment, extensions or renovations. The targets should contain requirements for an effective learning environment, comfort and health.

2. Detailed environmental targets

Detailed environmental targets should be drawn up for lighting, sound, ventilation and climate in all areas of the educational establishment for students and staff. The detailed environmental targets should be quantified as far as possible in order to be able to measure whether the targets have been achieved. For example, a quantifiable environmental target may be to achieve a background noise level of max. 30 dB(A) and 45 dB(C) in classrooms and a RASTI value (see glossary on page 106) of at least 0.75 for speech intelligibility. In order to achieve this level of speech intelligibility, a reverberation time of no more than 0.5 seconds is required. Then it is possible to address the practical measures based on an environmental plan in order to be able to evaluate and select methods and materials.

The environment agreed on?

Experience has shown that the end result sometimes differs considerably from what was intended in the original plans for an educational establishment. As a large number of interested parties are represented in a construction project, initially well thought-out functions can be diluted down as the project progresses. The most important functions in premises for education and learning must therefore be prioritised and specified at the programme work stage.

There are several reasons why things may not turn out as planned.

- It may be that targets and requirements were not clear from the outset, making the issue of responsibility unclear when choosing building materials or design solutions.
- Initial cost estimates may be inaccurate, leading to cutbacks in the quality of the specifications.

- Poor quality of construction could lead to environmental targets being lowered.
- The client may change their mind and therefore changes to the specifications need to be made.

There may be a number of sources of error during the building process. However, they must be eliminated as far as possible in order for the client to receive what they ordered and for the end users to receive an optimum learning environment.

An all too common sight in our schools: mould caused by damp has damaged the building materials and the rooms have to be cleaned at great cost. The school also has to be closed for the duration of these repairs.

Feasability stage

The feasability stage handles issues such as the type of operation, investment proposals and needs in terms of premises, equipment and installations. If the project is a newbuild, location, choice and type of land also enter into the equation. The feasability stage also includes studies of alternatives regarding location, etc.

Programme work (Project planning)

Programme work provides an analysis of functional requirements. A building/project programme is drawn up and forms the basis for the design work. The programme may contain a working environment programme and a technical programme containing requirements for lighting, indoor climate, noise levels, etc. The aim is to give the client/user the opportunity to specify the project's functions and budget so that the designers can interpret these requirements and provide a cost estimate. This stage is vital to the future finances and quality of the project. At this point a general plan is drawn up.

Design

Demands and requirements specified in the programme documents are transformed in the design stage into technical specifications and drawings which, depending on the type of contract chosen, will form the basis for negotiations and construction in the next stage. Building plans are drawn up. These describe how the building and the technical systems will be designed. Finally, working drawings, detailed specifications of the building are produced. The client has overall responsibility but is aided by experts.

Contract procurement and tendering

Procurement means that after a tendering procedure, one or more construction companies are appointed to the project. There are different kinds of contract. One is the standard (general) contract, in which the client or architect (acting on behalf of his employer – the client) oversees the appointment of a main contractor to be responsible for the whole project – who will then appoint sub-contractors. The client, or architect on behalf of the client, may also select the various contractors individually – this is called a shared (divided) contract – in which case a project manager is often appointed who is responsible to the architect/client. Finally, there is also a form of design and build contract where a contractor is responsible for both the construction and the detailed design. The client or architect (on behalf of the client) hands over responsibility and control of the construction project before the working drawings and system choices are finished.

Construction (production)

The aim of the construction work is to produce a building within the agreed time and budget and of the right quality. A contractual survey ensures that the contract has been fulfilled. The client has to check that it has received what it paid for and the facilities manager and users have to understand how the building is to be cared for.

Facilities Management (user phase)

Facilities management covers the use and maintenance of the finished building. It is important to point out the importance of taking into account maintenance, care and life cycle costs during the design stage.

Various stages of the building process
(which can vary in order depending on the contract awarded)

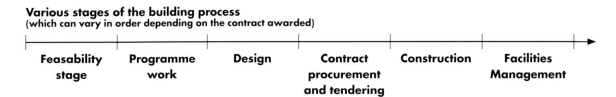

| Feasability stage | Programme work | Design | Contract procurement and tendering | Construction | Facilities Management |

Major need for good advice

By David J. MacKenzie, lecturer and research fellow at the Department of Building Engineering and Surveying at Heriot-Watt University, Edinburgh.

There is a major need for good advice on acoustics issues for all those involved in planning and designing educational buildings.

Several slightly alarming facts came out of discussions with a group of school designers working on planning educational environments.

"It became apparent, for example, that the group was unaware of any existing noise sources in the area surrounding the schools. In fact, a number of the schools are located in areas with busy roads and disturbing air traffic. The design of the schools did not take the environmental noise level into consideration, having large glazed areas facing existing sources of noise. The design of some schools had not made use of available expertise on indoor noise reduction. The group was unaware of the special needs of children with impaired hearing or vision. They also had little knowledge of recommended acoustic criteria.

Knowledge is out there but not information

It is currently possible to effectively reduce noise, create good room acoustics and achieve good speech intelligibility. The problem is that many of those who have a stake in designing educational environments often lack the relevant expertise and knowledge to do so.

It is therefore vital that:

Architects and designers of educational buildings understand:
– the basic guidelines on acoustics in schools.
– the importance of good acoustics in teaching spaces in general.
– the needs and requirements of children with special needs and how the incorporation of these children into mainstream education can be greatly assisted by good design.
– the potential detrimental effect that poor acoustics can have on a child's education.

Teachers, educators, etc. understand that:
– good acoustics in a teaching space are important for general wellbeing.
– a quieter teaching environment creates a calmer atmosphere.
– there is no need to raise your voice unnecessarily to make yourself heard in quieter classrooms. This also reduces the risk of the throat being damaged.

Parents of children at school realise that:
– the design of classrooms and inadequate room acoustics can be detrimental to learning.
– a noisy school environment can lead to a reduction in the ability of children to correctly hear what is being said by teachers and others.
– pupils and students appreciate improved room acoustics and speech intelligibility.

The authorities should be made to realise:
– the importance of including room acoustics in the planning and designing of educational environments.
– that acoustics issues should be taken into account at an early stage of the planning.
– that poor acoustics have an adverse effect on both teachers and pupils.

There is tremendous need to provide adequate guidance for those involved with educational buildings. From an acoustics point of view, this begins at the very design stages of a new school through to the every day running of an existing school irrespective of its size or type."

Points to remember:

- Difficult tasks, which are common in education, are particularly sensitive to noise.

- An indoor temperature far exceeding 20°C makes people tired and prevents them from concentrating.

- An efficient flow of air in the classroom is crucial for effective learning.

- Allergy sufferers and other hypersensitive people are particularly affected by a poor indoor environment.

- Pain, tiredness and depression can be due to stress caused by deficiencies in the working environment.

- Muscle tension and reduced nerve function can be caused by incorrect movement patterns and working positions, poor lighting or noise.

- It is important to try to achieve even and sufficient lighting across the whole room.

- Avoid glare from surfaces, windows etc.

- Light helps us feel awake and alert or tired and depressed.

- Well thought-out architecture and well-planned colour schemes and design language are the cornerstones on which a pleasant workplace is built.

- Logic and order can be created using colour.

- The choice of surface materials has a major impact on the perception of the room and colour environment.

- Plan in good time for a good indoor environment and working environment in conjunction with a newbuild, redevelopment, extension or refurbishment.

- The ability to achieve value for money is the major factor in the early stages of the building process.

- Set environmental targets from the start.

References – Learning requires a holistic approach to the indoor environment

Andersson, Johnny (1998). *Akustik & buller: en praktisk handbok (Acoustics and noise – a practical handbook)*. AB Svensk Byggtjänst. (in Swedish)

Bodén, Hans & Carlsson, Ulf & Glav, Ragnar & Wallin, H.P. & Åbom, Mats (1999). *Ljud och vibrationer (Sound and Vibrations)*. Kungliga Tekniska Högskolan, Institutionen för Farkostteknik, Marcus Wallenberg Laboratoriet för Ljud- och Vibrationsforskning (Royal Institute of Technology, Department of Vehicle Engineering, Marcus Wallenberg Laboratory for Sound and Vibration Research). (in Swedish)

Bodin, Anders (2000). *Om byggprocessen (About the building process)*. Paper/Bodin. (in Swedish)

Boverket & Arbetarskyddsstyrelsen (The Swedish National Board of Building, Planning and Housing & The Swedish National Board of Occupational Health) (edited by Hellberg, Annika) (1996). *Att se, höra och andas i skolan: en handbok om skolans innemiljö (Seeing, hearing and breathing in schools – a handbook on the indoor environment of schools)*. Publikationsservice. (in Swedish)

Byggforskningsrådet (Swedish Building Research Council)/Andersson, Sven & Borg, Thomas & Djurstedt, Bengt & Gulliksson, Hans & Igelström, Leif & Jonson, Jan-Olof & Lindstam, Martin & Olsson, Stefan & Starby, Lars (1992). *Bra innemiljö i skolan (Good indoor environments in schools)*. Byggforskningsrådet/Förlagshuset Gothia. (in Swedish)

Folkhälsoinstitutets allergiprogram (1999) (Swedish National Institute of Public Health's allergy programme). *Ren luft på kontoret (Clean air in the office)*. Alprosen (4/99) Folkhälsoinstitutet. (in Swedish)

Folkhälsoinstitutet (Swedish National Institute of Public Health) (2000). *De sex stegen för en sund skola: vägledning om innemiljö vid planering och förvaltning (Six steps for a healthy school: a guide on the indoor environment in planning and building management)*. Förlagshuset Gothia. (in Swedish and English)

Hannaford, Carla (1998). *Lär med hela kroppen: inlärning sker inte bara i huvudet (Smart moves)*. Brain Books. (in Swedish and English)

Holm, Birgitta & Hult, Marie (1999). *Projekteringsguide för en god innemiljö i skolor – förstudie (Planning guide for good indoor environments in schools – preliminary study)*. Byggforskningsrådet (Swedish Building Research Council). (in Swedish)

Kirke-, utdannings- og forskningsdepartementet (Norwegian Ministry of Education, Research and Church Affairs) (1995). *Skoleanlegg – forbedring og fornyelse. Grunnskole, videregående opplæring og voksenopplæring (Schools – improvement and renewal)*. Kommuneforlaget. (in Norwegian)

Laike, Torbjörn/Environmental Psychology Unit, School of Architecture, Lund Institute of Technology, Sweden (1997). *The impact of daycare environments on children's mood and behaviour*. Scandinavian Journal of Psychology, 1997, 38, 209-218. (in English)

Lys & Optik/Lysteknisk Selskab ((Delta division for) Light & Optics/Danish Illumination Engineering Society) (1993). *God og energirigtig skolebelysning (Good energy-efficient school lighting)*. Lysteknisk Selskab. (in Danish)

MacKenzie, David J. (2000). *Classroom acoustics*. Paper/MacKenzie. (in English)

NUTEK (Swedish National Board for Industrial and Technical Development) (1994). *Programkrav, belysning i skolor: Programkrav för god och energieffektiv belysning i skolor (Programme requirements for lighting in schools)*. NUTEK, Effektivare energianvändning. (in Swedish)

Rasmussen, Steen Eiler (1999). *Experience architecture*. MIT Press. (in English)

Schick, August & Meis, Markus & Reckhardt, Carsten (edited by) (2000). *Contributions to Psychological Acoustics; Results of the eighth Oldenburg symposium on psychological acoustics*. Bibliotheks- und Informationssystem der Universität Oldenburg. (in English)

Svenska Kommunförbundet (Swedish Association of Local Authorities) & Fahlin, Per & Andersson, Sven (1997). *Upphandling av sunda hus: redovisning av erfarenheter från Malmö stad samt ett 50-tal kommuner och landsting (The procurement process of healthy buildings)*. Svenska Kommunförbundet. (in Swedish)

Söderberg, Jan (1992). Byggnadsekonomi; *Byggprocessen i samhället (Building economics, the building process in society)*. Institutionen för byggnadsekonomi, Lunds Tekniska Högskola (Department of Construction Management, Lund Institute of Technology, Sweden). (in Swedish)

"One day man will be forced to fight noise as relentlessly as cholera and the plague."

Robert Koch, discoverer of the tuberculosis bacillus

Sound in the learning environment

Speech and hearing – the be all and end all

Speech dominates the majority of learning situations. The quality of the room's acoustics can therefore help determine whether teaching is sucessful or not.

From the dawn of time, man has used sound to communicate. Knowledge has passed from mouth to mouth, parents teach their children, who teach their children, and so on. Masters pass on professional information to apprentices who one day will become masters themselves. Teachers teach their pupils, who express this newly learned information in words, for example, by answering the teacher's questions.

Speech becomes an art form

The oral tradition was highly developed in the cultures of the ancient world. Knowledge vital to the survival of the culture was passed on by means of the spoken word.

In ancient Greece, speech was refined into an art form, giving birth to rhetoric. The Greeks discovered that an eloquent speaker could both pass on information and change the attitude of listeners.

The spoken word is the most important aspect in learning situations

The spoken word dominates in the majority of learning situations. If teaching is to succeed, everyone naturally has to be able to hear what is being said. In today's society the importance of hearing is often underestimated and visual impressions tend to dominate. Information primarily based on listening has become less important but, despite this, we spend the entire day listening. The hearing organ conveys sound to the brain even when we are asleep. While our field of vision is restricted to 180 degrees, our ears register sound from every direction. **We have the ability to identify what we hear, the direction from which the sound is coming and the approximate distance to the sound source.** The hearing function is unique and performs a unique task. If your hearing is poor, you are forced to put extra effort into understanding words. Often those with poor hearing are unable to understand the context of a conversation and are therefore unable to form the necessary connections with existing knowledge. Some decide not to listen at all,

We use speech and hearing to exchange knowledge, thoughts, opinions and experiences. Hearing is most important for the development of personality and for co-existence. Good hearing is also required for the development of our ability to speak.

resulting in a failure of the teaching process. What was to have been the starting point for the next lesson instead risks becoming a mass of questions and, in the worst cases, a complete blank.

A poor sound environment and poor hearing not only lessens the effectiveness of teaching but also has a negative physical and psychological impact on students and staff. The working environment is not ideal.

Today the knowledge and technology are available to create perfect room acoustics. The purpose of this chapter is to highlight and explain the basic factors which determine the quality of room acoustics and thus affect the way we experience sound.

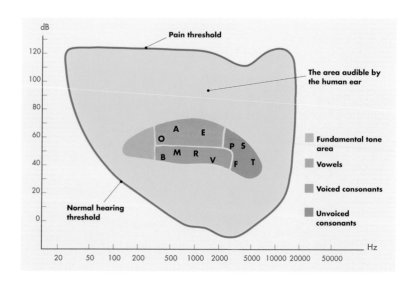

Generating speech

Speech occurs by air being forced past the vocal chords, which then begin to vibrate. The vibrations become a fundamental tone, which is reinforced in the oral and nasal cavity. The more air forced past the vocal chords per time interval, the stronger the sound – it is here that the volume at which we speak is determined. The frequency range of the fundamental tone varies from person to person depending, among other things, on sex and age. The voices of women and children tend to have a lighter tone than those of men. The fundamental tone in human speech is in the frequency range 125 – 250 Hz.

By placing the tongue and the lips in different positions we form the different sounds we call letters – vowels and voiced and unvoiced consonants. The vowels (a, e, o, i, u) are a direct extension of the fundamental tone and are relatively strong compared to the voiced consonants (b, d, m, etc.). The energy of the vowels primarily lies in the range 250 – 2,000 Hz and that of voiced consonants in the range 250 – 4,000 Hz. Unvoiced consonants (f, s, t, etc.) vary considerably in strength and lie in the frequency range 2,000 – 8,000 Hz. Consonant clusters such as the "sh" sound are also in this range. To be able to understand speech clearly, it is therefore important to have good hearing across the entire range of frequencies from 125 – 8,000 Hz. If one's hearing in this area is poor, this has a direct impact on one's ability to understand speech (see "Hearing impairment – an invisible problem" on page 86).

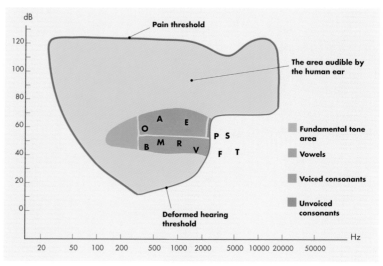

When hearing is impaired, it is common to lose the ability to understand consonants which often contain little sound energy and lie in the frequency range 2,000 – 8,000 Hz.

Generating and understanding speech

By Carsten Ruhe, acoustician,
Taubert und Ruhe GmbH, Germany

Commonly confused phonemes in German

	Easy to understand	Confused with
Lips forward, teeth together	sch	st, tz
Mouth wide open	a	ei, ä, h
Lips together	m	b, p
Tongue up, underside visible	l	n, d, t
Top teeth on bottom lip	f	v, w
Lips forward, teeth not visible	o	ö, u, ü
Movement from "a" towards "u"	au	
Mouth wide, teeth together	e	i, s, ä
(difficult to understand)		i, s, ß, d, t
(very difficult or impossible to understand)		g, k, ng, h, r, ch, j

The fundamental tones of speech (the "grating" sound from the vocal chords) vary very little during speech. On the other hand, the timbre created using the position of the lips, the teeth and the uvula, and which depends on the phoneme being pronounced at that particular time, changes considerably.

As shown by the diagram, the majority of the energy of the darkly resonating vowel "U", [u:], lies in the frequency range 200 – 600 Hz (the first formant). Parts of the considerably lighter vowel "I", [i:], are also in the high frequency range between 2,000 and 5,000 Hz (the second formant). Many consonants, primarily sibilants and plosives, are very explosive in character. For example, the energy in the German phoneme "SCH", [ʃ], is primarily in the frequency range 1,600 to 8,000 Hz and that of the considerably stronger German phoneme "TZ", [ts], in the frequency range 5,000 to 15,000 Hz. Sounds commonly confused by those with impaired hearing are shown in the table.

Sound volume and information

While the vowels create the sound volume of speech, it is the consonants which are the bearers of information.

This can be demonstrated in a very simple way, leave out the vowels when you whisper and it is still possible for the information to be heard in its entirety.

Understanding speech

The hearing of people with good hearing is optimally adapted to be able to receive information. *Especially in the frequency range where the important sibilants and plosives are found, the hearing threshold is very low,* in other words hearing is very sensitive in this range. This trend is reflected in DIN 45 630-2 [1], the result of an assessment of 70 people with German as their mother tongue. According to studies by Tomatis [2], the hearing thresholds of people with English, French or Italian as their mother tongue are completely different. In this case it is possible that custom or practice has been superimposed on developmental characteristics.

[1] DIN 45 630-2 *Grundlagen der Schallmessung, Normalkurven gleicher Lautstärkepegel* (The basics of sound measurement, normal curves with the same sound volume), September 1967
[2] Tomatis, Alfred, *Das Ohr und das Leben* (The ear and life); Walter, Düsseldorf, 1995

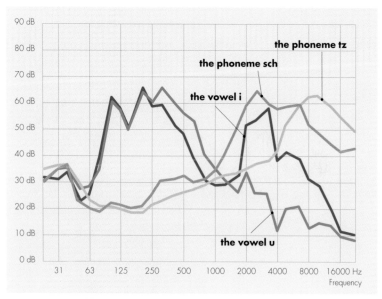

The phoneme tz
the phoneme sch
the vowel i
the vowel u

The spectrum for the German vowels U, [u:], and I [i:]. The vowel U contains only the first formant between 200 and 600 Hz. The vowel I also contains the second formant between 2,000 and 5,000 Hz.

The spectrum for the German phonemes SCH, [ʃ], and TZ, [ts]. The main energy in the SCH sound lies between 1,600 and 8,000 Hz. In the sharper phoneme TZ it lies between 5,000 and 15,000 Hz.

Childhood learning is vital

By Sharon L. Airey, research fellow, Institute of Education, Stirling University, Scotland.
Formerly researcher at the Department of Building Engineering and Surveying, Heriot-Watt University, Edinburgh

It is fair to say that we never stop learning but learning is particularly important in the early years. I was impressed when a classroom which was acoustically treated produced better results in subjective listening tests.

"The quality of formal and informal education in childhood can have a drastic effect on the rest of a person's life.

Today's parents will often choose a school for their child depending on its location, reputation and teaching methods. The physical environment, beyond immediate appearances plays little or no role in their decision. However, it has been shown that the physical environment of a school can have a significant effect on a child and the quality of education they receive. This is particularly true of room acoustics.

During my time at teacher training college I was never once taught about the acoustic environment in the classroom. Once I began teaching I worked as a supply teacher, moving from one school to the next. Some classrooms were always difficult to work in, always noisy and stressful, whilst others seemed to have a much quieter and calmer atmospheres. I instinctively knew that this had little to do with the class of children but more to do with the rooms themselves. It was only after having studied the science of acoustics and working on a major study carried out at Heriot-Watt University in Edinburgh that I realised these classrooms had poor acoustics. The classrooms I found difficult to teach in, for example, had high plaster ceilings, large windows, bare floorboards and little or no absorbency whatsoever.

Building techniques are advancing – acoustics are standing still

Even with all the amazing scientific and technological advancements in the last century, schools are still being designed and built without considering acoustics. Sometimes many of the newer schools have just as poor if not worse acoustics than older ones. This is shocking when the opportunity of creating good room acoustics does exist.

I was amazed at the drastic improvement in results after installing an acoustic ceiling. Listening tests showed clear improvements in speech intelligibility for every single pupil. One of the most impressive improvements in the listening environment achieved by the introduction of an acoustic ceiling was the total elimination of "dead spots" (locations in the classroom where little or no speech from the teacher's voice would be intelligible).

Acoustic problems can only be addressed by visiting a school, talking to staff and students and carefully studying the circumstances in every individual case. Experience shows that they are always different."

Acoustics – some basic principles

"Acoustics" is the term for the study of sound and how sound is experienced. Acoustics is divided into several specialist areas. This chapter looks primarily at room acoustics.

The word acoustics comes from the Greek akoustikos ("to do with hearing") and akouo ("to hear").

Acoustics is usually divided into the following areas:

Physical acoustics – studies the behaviour of sound waves.

Physiological acoustics – studies the hearing processes which convert sound waves to nerve impulses.

Psychoacoustics – studies the way sound is experienced.

Electroacoustics – sound reproduction techniques.

Musical acoustics – focuses on how musical sounds are produced and experienced.

Building acoustics – studies technical and physical sound problems in conjunction with construction techniques, i.e. sound insulation and issues concerning sound reflection and absorption. **This field includes room acoustics.**

Sound – where does it come from?

A sound is created when the particles in a medium – a gas (usually air), solid or liquid – are set moving and forced out of a state of rest. This happens, for example, when a teacher speaks and his or her vocal chords produce (audible) pressure variations in the air.

Speaking causes pressure variations in the air.

Sound travels in air at a speed of approximately 340 metres per second (compare this with the speed of sound in other materials, page 70).

Sound is a form of energy like light, movement and heat. The sound spreads like a wave and is a mechanical vibration, unlike light and radio waves, for example, which are electromagnetic waves. Sound can therefore only spread in a physical medium such as air. A room with no air, a vacuum, does not allow sound to propagate.

When the physical sound waves are captured by the outer ear (our human antenna) they are first amplified through its unique architecture, then the pressure variations are converted in various stages to sound sensations (see page 80, "The ear and hearing").

Frequency and frequency bands

Just like waves in water, sound waves move at a certain speed past a fixed point. The frequency of the waves is the number of peaks or troughs which pass this point in a second. **The frequency is given in hertz (Hz).** The higher the number, the lighter the tone and vice versa (treble and bass, respectively).

Frequencies below and above the frequency range which can normally be heard by humans (20 – 20,000 Hz) are known as infrasound and ultrasound, respectively.

Frequency bands are used to give a practical description of frequency distribution between various kinds of sound. Each band contains a fixed number of frequencies. The most common bands are the octave band and the one-third octave band, which is narrower than the octave band.

Sound pressure and decibels

Sound pressure, or sound pressure level, is the result of the pressure variations in the air achieved by the sound waves. The lowest sound pressure which can be heard by humans is called the **hearing threshold,** the highest which can be endured is known as the **pain threshold.** Sound

The speed of sound

Type of medium	Speed m/s
Vacuum (no air particles)	0
Rubber	50
Air	340
Cork	500
Water (20° C)	1,484
Brick	2,800
Wood (pine – along direction of fibres)	3,400
Concrete	4,000
Steel	5,100
Glass	5,200

(Source: "Akustik & Buller. En praktisk handbok" (Acoustics and noise. A practical handbook) J Andersson. Swedish Building Centre)

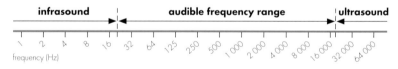

Infrasound is frequencies under 20 Hz, ultrasound is frequencies over 20,000 Hz. Audible sound lies between these parameters.

pressure at the pain threshold is a million times greater than that at the hearing threshold.

To avoid processing speech covering so wide a range, a compressed, logarithmic scale is used based on the decibel unit (dB). Here the lowest sound pressure level has the value of 0 dB (the hearing threshold) while the pain threshold has the value of approximately 120 dB.

If the values are added together on a logarithmic scale, the result differs from that on a linear scale. If two equally strong sound sources are added together, the combined sound pressure level does not double but increases by three decibels.

To better resemble the human ear, sound level meters are equipped with different filters, including A and C filters. These are designed to combine sound pressure levels for all frequencies to produce a single value, known as sound level. The sound level measured with an A filter is called dB(A) and is most common, while dB(C) places greater emphasis on low frequencies and better reflects the sound experienced by those with a hearing impairment.

Music, which is an important element of education, is a mixture of sound pressure at different frequencies (tones).

Mountainous landscapes enable sound to spread by echo. Over history this has been exploited for communication between people long distances apart and to herd cattle.

The arias sung by gondoliers are heard in all their glory between the high, reflecting façades of the houses of Venice which line the narrow canals. Water is an ideal surface for propagating sound.

In cathedrals sound remains as an echo for several seconds. This creates the sacred atmosphere sought in a religious setting. The priest consciously talks slowly so that his words reach the congregation without being drowned by the echo.

Echo – a plus and a minus

Outdoors, echo is something we have learned to use for both practical purposes and for our own great entertainment. Indoors, on the other hand, echo generally causes problems.

Outdoor acoustics have created musical languages around the world. One example is yodelling in the European alpine countries. A similar musical form is the Swedish "kulning" used by the women of Dalarna to herd and call their cattle and to communicate with other farms. Kulning and yodelling developed through interplay with the landscape. This shrill and staccato form exploits the echo found in mountainous topography. Neither would be possible in the flat countryside of the Netherlands, for example.

In Italy it is likely that Italian gondoliers learned early on to exploit the echo on the narrow canals of Venice passing between the tall, tightly packed buildings. The environment itself inspires song.

Problems often arise indoors

Indoors, echo can constitute a problem and various solutions have to be applied, for example, so that speech can be understood without effort.

Throughout history churches have also acted as classrooms for purposes other than the purely theological. Current requirements in terms of room acoustics and teaching are not particularly compatible with the echo in churches. Organ music, on the other hand, is often adapted to church acoustics. If the music is to be enjoyed, the tempo and the length of notes has to be selected on the basis of the particular acoustics of the church, as Bach and Handel knew. Similarly, priests have been forced to speak slowly and almost over-clearly so that their words reach the congregation.

With the Reformation, knowledge and teaching became more important. The spoken word took on increased importance and more attention was paid to the negative effects of long reverberation time (see next page) in teaching situations.

Reverberation time

In a room the sound waves are reflected (bounce) off of surfaces such as walls and ceilings, **causing one source of sound to become several. All the sounds in a room therefore have a particular reverberation time, in other words the sound is heard for a while after the sound source has been turned off.** The sound lives on in the form of an echo, a phenomenon known as reverberation.

Reverberation time is the time it takes for the sound pressure level to fall by 60 dB after the source of the sound has ceased. In theory the reverberation time can be calculated based on the volume of the room using Sabine's formula. Reverberation times are normally described in six frequency ranges (octave bands) between 125 and 4,000 Hz.

Early reflections of sound (e.g. via a blackboard) are good. These produce an impression of space, help to reinforce and clarify speech and convey the feeling that the voice carries. These reflections are particularly important for those at the back of a room where the direct sound is muted if the teacher or lecturer is facing the board. Direct sound is the sound which carries, for example, from the teacher's mouth directly to the students' ears and is crucial to good speech intelligibility. Too long a reverberation time and late reflections, on the other hand, impair speech intelligibility.

Sabine's formula:

A theoretical and approximate reverberation time in premises covering less than 1,000 m³ can be calculated using the following two formulae:

If the average absorption factor (αm) is less than 0.3, Sabine's formula is used:

$$T = \frac{0.16 \times V}{A}$$

where T is the reverberation time in seconds, V is the volume of the premises in m³ and A is the total absorption in m² sabin (the absorption is defined as the absorption factor x surface in m²).

If (αm) is greater than 0.3, the Sabine-Eyring formula is used:

$$T = \frac{0.16 \times V}{-S \ln(1 - \alpha m)}$$

where S is the total surface area in m², ln is the natural logarithm.

The reverberation time in large rooms cannot be calculated using the above formulae.

Wallace Clement Sabine, (1868–1919), American physicist and the inventor of Sabine's formula. The only equipment he used to measure reverberation times and create his formula, which has since become famous and is now used all around the world, were his ears and a normal stopwatch.

Speech intelligibility

Long reverberation times mean that a word does not have time to finish reverberating before the next word reaches the listener, which causes poor speech intelligibility.

Our ability to comprehend sound is also affected by the relationship between the strength of the sound and the strength of the background noise (ventilation noise, footsteps, talking, etc.) which is always present.

The geometry of the room, the acoustic characteristics of its boundary surfaces, the voice of the speaker and the hearing of the listener are other factors which affect speech intelligibility.

A RASTI value of at least 0.75 is an appropriate requirement for a normal classroom. This is possible to achieve if the background noise level is a maximum of 30 dB(A) and 45 dB(C) and the reverberation time does not exceed 0.5 seconds.

Measurement methods

Speech intelligibility can be measured in several ways. In general we refer to RASTI values (RApid Speech Transmission Index) which are measured on a scale of 0 – 1, with 1 being best. As well as the RASTI method, STI (Speech Transmission Index), AI (Articulation Index), Early Energy Fraction and Articulation Loss of Consonants (%Alcons) are also used. These various methods are described in more detail on page 106 (Glossary).

The Pantheon in Rome, from 120 AD, with its concrete dome spanning 43.4 meters, remained unsurpassed until the nineteenth century. The ceiling, a type of cavity absorber, was an early and advanced solution to create a good sound environment. Visitors still marvel at the unique acoustics.

Sound absorption
– a question of limiting sound reflection

Sitting on the beach and listening to the waves lapping at the rocks is relaxing for the soul. But it is good neither for the ear nor the soul to be forced to listen to sound waves which bounce between hard surfaces indoors, e.g. in a classroom.

Walls, ceilings, floors and other surfaces in a room act as acoustic mirrors. When you click your fingers in a room, the click is an "original sound source". It is copied by new sound sources, echoes, arising when the sound waves encounter the various acoustic mirrors in the room, amplifying the sound (more on echoes and reverberation time on page 74).

Absorbers reduce the echo effect

The use of absorbers can reduce the echo effect and shorten rever-beration times. The absorber does exactly what its name suggests: it absorbs – "sucks in" – the sound.

The section "Acoustics – some basic principles" (page 69) explains how **sound is a form of energy.** Energy can neither be created nor destroyed, it can only be converted from one form to another. **Sound, for example, can become heat,** according to the **energy principle** used in physics.

When a sound wave encounters porous material, for example, some of the sound energy is reflected at the surface while the rest enters the material, it is slowed down by friction and is converted into heat energy. Other sound energy passes through the material and disappears, i.e. is transmitted, out the other side, **so reducing the reverberation time and lowering the sound level. These are the two most important tasks of the absorber.**

The more the material absorbs, the less sound energy it reflects. The term absorption factor (α) is used in this context. If this is 1.0, it means that 100% of the sound energy which encounters the absorber is transformed.

Different types of absorber

Sound-absorbent material and structures can be divided into two main groups depending on the way they work:

1) Porous absorbers (e.g. glass wool and stone wool products, highly porous felt products, fabric, etc.) work by means of the friction which

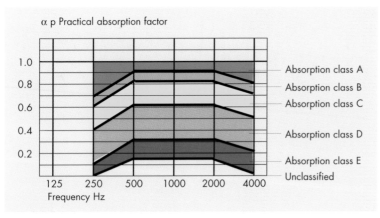

The ability of the sound absorber is measured in line with the international standard EN ISO 354, and is classified according to the international standard EN ISO 11654 on the basis of its absorption factor, i.e. its ability to "absorb the sound", into absorption classes A, B, C, D and E, with A providing the best absorption.

Acoustics in this gymnasium are handled using an acoustic ceiling.

arises inside the material. The friction causes some of the sound energy to be converted into heat. A thick porous material converts larger amounts of energy than a thinner one. The part of the sound energy which is not converted is transmitted out on the other side of the absorber.

2) Resonance absorbers mute the sound level through resonance oscillations. The sound waves continue to vibrate the enclosed volume of air, friction arises and heat energy is formed. This type of absorber is most effective in narrow frequency ranges. Resonance absorbers are divided into:

    a) cavity absorbers (e.g. breeze blocks placed on edge),

    b) membrane absorbers – a sealed sheet or membrane with air behind it.

    Both a) and b) can be more effective if the space behind the absorber is fitted with a porous absorber. This allows the absorber to work in a wider frequency band, increasing its practical use.

Absorbers in rooms

Curtains, carpets, and upholstered furniture naturally act as sound absorbers. However, they produce a far from desirable effect in terms of reverberation time and RASTI values due to the fact that they only absorb the high frequencies of sound outside the register of speech.

To achieve optimum room acoustics, sound absorbers should be placed on the largest uninterrupted free space in the room, the ceiling. Sometimes wall absorbers are also required.

Placing the absorbers high up in the room reduces the risk of mechanical damage.

An air gap can also be created in the space above a suspended acoustic ceiling. The air gap works with the acoustic ceiling and increases the absorption effect, particularly at low frequencies.

Sound absorbers in the ceiling also counter the problem of sound being reflected from the angles of the ceiling.

What are good room acoustics?

School lessons held out in the open air enjoy the best "room acoustics", however the lack of walls and ceilings naturally limits well-being in other respects. People who are used to being inside cosy buildings might find sitting outside during a lesson a bit primitive. But it's far from primitive in terms of "room acoustics".

Using the sky as a ceiling is the ultimate solution in terms of "room acoustics" with 100% absorption. For obvious reasons we tend to have to surround ourselves with walls and ceilings, primarily as protection from the weather. This means we have to take into account and resolve the problems which arise in terms of noise and reverberation times.

The ear and hearing

The majority of knowledge goes in through the ear. The ingenious architecture of the ear takes the sound step by step into the centre of hearing.

Sound waves are captured by the ear and registered by the brain after having passed the three main parts of the hearing organ:

1) the outer ear and the auditory meatus
2) the middle ear and
3) the inner ear

The shape of the outer ear and the auditory meatus acoustically amplifies the incoming sound waves. The mechanical vibration caused by the (amplified) sound waves causes the ear drum to vibrate. From the ear drum the sound proceeds to the middle ear. Here are the hammer, anvil and stirrup bone, three small auditory bones (together weighing approximately 60 mg) which are connected together. In the middle ear the sound waves/vibrations are amplified further as the surface of the ear drum is about 20 times the size of the oval window to which the stirrup bone is attached.

The ear drum is kept tight by one of the two small muscles of the inner ear. The other prevents excessively strong movements in the stirrup bone.

Sound takes shape in Corti's organ

The vibrations from the ear drum are transmitted via the auditory bones and the oval window in the inner ear. This is where the cochlea is found, a spiral-shaped canal of bone with two wide and one narrow elastic membrane canals. The narrow canal contains the actual **sensory organ, Corti's organ,** which is about 30 mm long and a tenth as wide at its widest point.

From the oval window an upper canal runs to the top of the cochlea. When the stirrup bone presses the oval window inwards, the movement is transmitted through the fluid system of the inner ear to the top of the cochlea. Here the pressure wave turns around and goes back via the lower canal to the round window which faces onto the middle ear. The round window is an elastic membrane which bulges out when pressure increases in the fluid system of the cochlea, evening out the pressure.

The basilar membrane in the narrow canal moves when the fluid and the round window do. It is here that the sound sensation begins to take shape. Corti's organ rests on the basilar membrane and contains

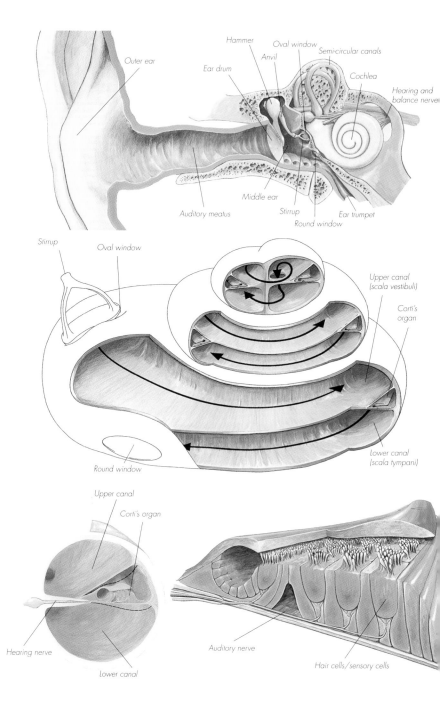

The anatomy of hearing
(Dalloz Safety AB)

approximately 25,000 **sensory cells,** which have feelers, which is why they are often called **hair cells.** As the basilar membrane vibrates, the sensory hairs bend when they come into contact with a covering membrane immediately above. This creates mechanical stimuli in the cells, which are transferred via biochemical processes to the auditory nerve. This then passes on the stimuli as electrical impulses along chains of nerve cells and nerve fibres to the auditory centre, which is located in the cerebral cortex. Sound arises in the consciousness here.

The hair cells hear different tones

If all the nerve cells were stimulated at the same time, we would not be able to distinguish one sound from another. This is why the oscillations are strongest next to the oval window at high frequencies. The higher up towards the top of the cochlea you go, the lower the frequencies to which the hair cells react.

Far from all sound is picked up by the human ear. **People hear only a small proportion of all sounds to which they are exposed.** Some sounds are too high or too low for us to hear. In principle humans hear sounds in the frequency range of 20 – 20,000 Hz. The ear is most sensitive in the frequency range 1,000 – 4,000 Hz. When we speak we do so in the frequency range 125 – 8,000 Hz.

Hair cells can't work miracles

As stated above, sound occurs when a sound wave is guided into the ear, causing the basilar membrane in the cochlea to vibrate. Vibration occurs at that point in the cochlea which corresponds to the given frequency. The vibrations cause the hair cells to bend at that point. If the same hair cells are often stimulated, their metabolism can be disrupted and the cells temporarily stop working, resulting in hearing impairment. However, the cells recover if they are allowed to rest. **If, on the other hand,**

the stress continues day after day, the blood supply to the cells and their metabolism will change such that they finally stop working altogether, with incurable hearing impairment as a result.

Not only does hearing impairement make it harder to hear sounds but the sounds heard are of a poorer quality. This is because the ear hears tones of different frequencies more or less well and does not pick up increases and decreases in the strength of the sound naturally. A person with a hearing impairment therefore hears the distorted sound and so finds it difficult to listen to speech or enjoy music.

One type of hearing damage which is attracting increasing attention and is to a certain extent noise related is tinnitus – hissing, buzzing and other continuous sounds in the ear. Researchers disagree on what causes tinnitus, a physically harmless (but mentally unpleasant) and in principle incurable disorder. Whiplash and stress are some suspected causes of tinnitus, as is loud noise.

Besides problems hearing sound, even a slight hearing loss can result in difficulties concentrating, headaches, tension and other symptoms.

Reactions to sound

Human hearing is not adapted to the noisy sound environment of the 21st century. Today's sources of sound force themselves on us, irritate us and make us ill. We cannot turn off our hearing, but we can learn how we are affected physically and mentally by the sounds which surround us.

Our ancestors were used to listening to signals from nature. That rustling in the bushes – a dangerous animal? A call from the jungle – a cry for help?

In today's society, we are also surrounded by other (and for us unnatural) sounds, but while the source of the sounds may have changed, human hearing has not. What's more, when exposed to various kinds of sound, we still instinctively react as our ancestors did.

Human hearing was originally tailored to the sounds of nature – no rumbling engines, no long reverberation or dangerously loud background noise.

When the human race was in its infancy, good hearing often meant the difference between life and death. Today, its most important role is interpersonal communication.

However, our way of instinctively reacting to sound is similar to that of our ancestors. We are still controlled by the warning function of our hearing – it has been part of us since the dawn of creation – and we can never turn our hearing off. Even during sleep, the brain registers sound. In an educational environment it is therefore vital to promote the sounds which need to be heard and to eliminate those which disturb us.

Three types of instinctive response to sound

People's instinctive response to sound is generally divided into **orientation, surprise and defence reactions.**

In an orientation response, weak or medium-strength sounds make us look spontaneously in the direction of the sound source. Our body prepares to react and to receive and process information. Our own assessment of the sound is a major factor. We can accustom ourselves to certain sounds and prevent an orientation response because we have learnt what the sound means and chosen not to notice it. However, the brain receives the sound signals anyway, just as it does when we are sleeping, which means we are able to react subconsciously and automatically in an instinctive situation.

The surprise response arises on hearing a sudden and intense sound, possibly of a frightening nature. Your eyes blink, your mouth opens, your neck bends and your muscles tense. In less than a second your body freezes into position with shoulders hunched and knees bent. The surprise response often remains even when we can control the sound source. An experiment igniting hydrogen and oxygen in a chemistry lesson is likely to cause a reflex reaction in the teacher and pupils alike, and they will react in exactly the same way if the experiment is repeated. The stronger the sound, the more powerful the surprise response.

Pupils and teachers are exposed to noise and irrelevant sound which has an adverse mental impact.

Hearing is a factor in creating security.

The defensive response comes when we hear a threatening sound, the body prepares itself in various ways according to the fight or flight instinct. The brain goes to red alert, the senses sharpen and we prepare for rapid action. Our muscles tense and our pulse and breathing are affected, as is production of saliva and gastric acid. This third form of response is also incredibly difficult to suppress.

The right sound environment reduces the risk of an unnecessary response

This is why it is vital to create educational environments which do not activate the surprise and defensive responses. A situation where various sound sources more or less permanently engender these reflexes creates a problematic lack of concentration as well as unnecessary stresses on body and mind. To live in a safe environment is a fundamental human need.

Good room acoustics create security

Pupils in rowdy and noisy classrooms can start to behave badly. The noise helps to create general worry, restlessness and a sense that "when everyone else is playing up, I have the right to play up also". The teacher's ability to keep order in the classroom is undermined when the general sound level is high.

Hearing and being heard without extra strain makes people calmer and more secure.

Maslow's hierarchy of needs

Psychologist Abraham Maslow developed his famous hierarchy of needs on the basis of a total five levels of human need. The bottom level concerns our physical need for oxygen, water, food and sex. Next Maslow placed the human need for security. This second level has to do with how our five senses (vision, hearing, smell, taste and touch) work. Normal hearing provides safety/security by helping us discover and interpret our surroundings and communicate with them.

Hearing is especially important in learning environments. Hearing is a factor that creates security in terms of:

- being able to process a complex social existence with many other people
- hearing what is being taught, asked, answered, discussed and ordered
- understanding signals from bells, equipment, etc.
- orienting oneself

The situation becomes particularly critical for those with a hearing impairment. Not having the physical ability to understand sound correctly is irritating and creates a sense of isolation and reduced self-esteem.

Sound is part of our environment. French architect and acoustician Bernard Delage claims that in public areas sound must have a clear identity, an auditive code. Only then can people orient themselves and understand how, for example, a product is to be used. Examples of codes:

Signals: A bell ringing or the sound of a reversing lorry.

Guidance/information: the sounds from a computer game indicating success or failure.

Atmosphere: "Walls of sound" can be created by making a certain sound clearer than other sounds in the surrounding area, thus leading to the feeling that "this is a private area".

Hearing impairment
– an invisible problem

It tends not to be noticable that people have poor hearing. Many people with impaired hearing do not talk about their disability but suffer in silence.

Hearing damage is initially unnoticeable even to those affected. One day you discover that you can no longer hear birdsong. Gradually hearing loss begins to impinge on the critical speech area. The consonants vital to language disappear first, followed by the vowels.

Background noise disturbs those with impaired hearing more than others

A study (Crandell, 1993) showed that background noise made it harder for those with impaired hearing – in this case children – to understand speech. A group with normal hearing and a group with impaired hearing listened to speech at a normal conversational level of 65 dB under quiet conditions. The task was to listen to and repeat sentences. Those with normal hearing got almost every one correct and those with impaired hearing achieved a 96% success rate. The difference increased in line with the amount of "noise". With background noise of 71 dB, children with normal hearing understood almost 71% of what was said but the figure for those with a hearing impairment was only 38%.

YOU SHOULD CALL DAVE

YOU SHOULD CALL DAVE

YOU SHOULD CALL DAVE

YOU SHOULD CALL DAVE

90% of all those with a hearing impairment have suffered damage to the inner ear and the cochlea, primarily due to damage to a number of hair cells. This reduces the ability to hear certain frequencies. This problem cannot be resolved by a hearing aid, which only amplifies sound. This hearing damage creates problems which can be compared to reading a sentence where the letters and words are incomplete.

10% of people with a hearing impairment only have problems with weak sounds, not with the balance within the frequency range. Here a hearing aid is a more effective tool but correctly balanced room acoustics help even more.

Room acoustics are extra important for people with impaired hearing

For a hearing impaired person it is not only the size of the room which is disturbing, but the type of lighting (vision becomes more important when hearing is poor) and technical aids are also important. According to various studies room acoustics are vital if people with impaired hearing are to be able to function successfully and work efficiently.

Mother tongue? An important issue

Besides hearing impairment, the level of linguistic skill also makes special demands of the sound environment and the acoustics. For those studying foreign languages, and for children learning their own language, both normal hearing and the right acoustic conditions are required to understand sound correctly and benefit from the teaching.

Researchers Nabelek and Donahue tested the effect of reverberation on the understanding of consonants of native English speakers and immigrant Americans aged between 25 and 52. All those who had moved to the US had learned English in their teens and spoke with a slight accent. Without reverberation both groups demonstrated identical results in the speech intelligibility test. However, with increased reverberation times those who were not born in the US produced poorer results than those who were (see diagram on page 88).

For a person with impaired hearing learning English, the result can be that they might only hear the vowels   e   a   a o   e   a in the phrase The cat sat on the mat. An incomprehensible combination of letters, compared with hearing only the consonants: Th c t s t n th m t.

Perceptions of consonants

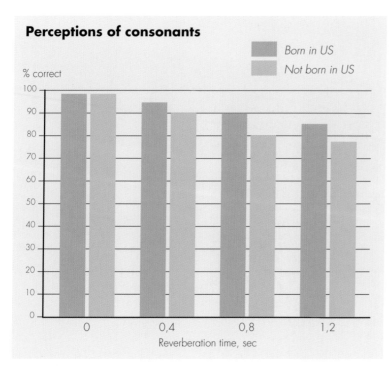

Legend: Born in US / Not born in US

% correct

Reverberation time, sec

Perceptions of consonants in reverberation by native and non native listeners, Nabelek & Donahue, 1984.

There are estimated to be about 8.7 million people in the UK who are deaf or hard of hearing. Of these, there are between 23,000 and 25,000 who are under the age of 15. They are in the phase of life where language is being developed, fundamental educational skills are obtained and social skills are being established. Not hearing properly easily results in a sense of isolation.

The sensitive child.

Examples of factors which affect children and demand good acoustics in learning environments:

- The loudness of the speech
- Concentration difficulties
- Cognitive development (cognitive abilities include memory and problem solving)
- Linguistic differences
- Linguistic development
- Lack of clarity in the speech of others
- Dyslexia (reading difficulties)
- Autism (being mentally cut off from the outside world)
- Upbringing/home environment
- Infections in airways and the auditory canal
- Bullying

The common cold can impair hearing by approximately −15 to −30 dB(A) compared with normal hearing, in the frequency range of speech 125 – 8,000 Hz. Fiellau-Kikolajsen discovered in 1983, "up to 95% of primary school children will suffer middle ear disease in the first 10 years". This results in a temporary hearing impairment. Coughs and colds are the main causes of temporary hearing loss.

All these groups have particularly great needs for an optimum sound environment:

People with:	*Estimated proportion of UK population:*
• *Permanent hearing impairment*	*approx. 15%*
• *Temporary hearing impairment (e.g. due to a cold, etc.)*	*approx. 20%*
• *Severe sight impairment (compensated for by hearing)*	*approx. 2%*
• *Difficulties concentrating*	*Maybe due to illness but also temporary, e.g. concentration can be disturbed by physical disorders which irritate, personal problems in general and a poor interior environment.*
• *Speech difficulties*	*approx. 7%*

Sound from every direction

Sound is formed everywhere there are people. We want to listen to some of these sounds but too many are experienced as noise. Sound waves are very good at travelling through the air and through buildings.

The illustration shows some examples of sources of sound and noise in or close to learning situations and how sound is spread.

1 Corridors and communal areas are very noisy. The sound travels down the length of the corridor and into classrooms through poorly insulated partitions and doors. Muffled and disturbing noise creeps into the rooms through the floor and joists.

2 Noise from workshops, music rooms, canteens and other noisy environments travels through walls and joists to classrooms.

3 Ventilation systems can transport sound between various rooms. Ventilation and air conditioning systems can create irritating low-frequency noise.

4 A lot of noise is created in classrooms from scraping chairs, squeaking, speaking, shouting and slamming desks.

5 Computers, printers and other equipment produce disturbing background noise.

6 Tubular fluorescent lamps which are not fitted with electronic ballasts can produce vibration in the fitting which in turn gives off low-frequency noise.

7 Noise from footsteps is common from wooden floors, for example. The sound can spread to rooms below through poorly insulated floor joists.

8 Playgrounds nearby can be sources of very disturbing noise.

9 Busy streets and roads and nearby airports are unsuitable surroundings for educational premises. Noise makes its way in through unsealed and poorly insulated windows and doors.

10 Factories close by can be a very irritating source of noise.

Noise and people

Dr Robert Koch, discoverer of the tuberculosis bacillus and one of history's greatest scientists, is said to have commented at the start of the 20th century: "One day man will be forced to fight noise as relentlessly as cholera and the plague."

The noise around us is harmful in a number of ways. It has an adverse effect on work, social interaction and, not least, the individual.

The section "The ear and hearing", page 80, describes how loud sounds and noise can damage hearing. However, noise also has a psychological impact on people.

Swedish professor Anders Kjellberg is one of those who has conducted research into noise. He identified three different psychological effects of noise.

The first is the subjective reaction – how the noise is perceived.

The second is the impact on performance. For example, noise (unwanted sound) reduces a person's ability to work well.

The third psychological effect is that noise can disturb and stress a person to the extent that physiological reactions arise in the form of increased heart rate and raised blood pressure. It is thought that long-term exposure to loud noise may lead to a permanent rise in blood pressure.

What is noise?

The term "noise" does not only refer to disturbingly loud levels of sound. **Noise is generally described as "unwanted sound".** Some sounds, for example sound levels above the pain threshold, are experienced as noise by everyone. However, according to the definition, there are other individual "pain thresholds" which often have to do with attitudes. For example many older people experience rock music as noise.

Noise is very disturbing. When concentration and good audibility is required, e.g. in learning situations, noise has to be reduced considerably. **It is important to screen off sources of noise in the property and isolate noise from outdoors** (see the section "Sounds which have an impact", page 28). **Noise arising in the premises in which one is located can partly be muted through sound absorption.**

Disturbing background noise includes:
- humming and buzzing heating/ventilation/air conditioning systems
- noisy machines and equipment
- conversations between people
- footsteps
- scraping chairs
- traffic noise

In public premises the general noise level has to be kept low by taking action at the source of sound and reducing the spread of the sound.

Children in noisy schools needed more time to complete jigsaws and were unsuccessful more often than children in quiet schools (Cohen et al. 1980, 1981). The results support the thesis that children in schools with chronic noise have lower patience levels and motivation.

Noise breeds noise

In a normal classroom background noise in the form of chatter and scraping chairs can easily reach strengths of 65 – 70 dB(A). To make oneself heard in this kind of environment one has to add a further 10 – 15 dB(A), which means having to shout. We say that noise breeds noise.

Noise which is not very loud can also be disturbing

The impact of noise depends mainly on the following factors:

- The noise level. This often plays a crucial role, although noise which is not very loud can be extremely disturbing, depending on the situation.
- The variation in the level and frequency of the noise and how predictable and controllable it is. Varying noise is more disturbing. Noise which you can control yourself, or which you know will occur, is easier to accept.
- The meaningfulness of the noise. Other people's speech, for example, attracts our attention more easily than meaningless sound.
- Type of work. Certain jobs can be carried out in a noisy environment, particularly monotonous monitoring tasks, as the sound keeps you awake. Long, complex tasks in which you have to deal with information from many sources at the same time are more difficult to carry out in a noisy environment.
- Necessity. If the noise is seen to be necessary, and so cannot be avoided, the psychological impact is reduced.

The monotonous low-frequency noise from equipment which regulates the internal climate is soporific. This results in us performing worse on more advanced tasks (Kjellberg et al, 1993).

Cognitive-based work and noise

According to several international reports, schools are generally felt to be noisy. At the same time, the school is the one environment in society created specifically for cognitive work.

An educational environment has two main sources of noise: external noise from the playground, transport (cars, etc.) and internal noise generated by teachers, pupils and technical equipment such as ventilation systems and computers.

Research shows that noise has a crucial impact on people's cognitive functions: alertness, memory, problem solving and decision making.

Comparatively simple cognitive tasks, e.g. basic counting (arithmetic), are not affected by noise to any great degree, but more difficult tasks are. If analysis of meaning or content is required, people are more easily disturbed, particularly if the background noise comprises of meaningful information such as speech. The quality or content of the source of the noise affects **performance and short-term memory** more than the sound pressure level (number of decibels). Irrelevant human speech is disturbing and affects performance and short-term memory even at low levels, while there are indications that prolonged exposure to noise has a stronger impact. No general differences have been discovered between women and men in this area.

Studies of long-term memory show it to be adversely affected by airport noise. The same studies also suggest that blood pressure increases in children exposed to this noise.

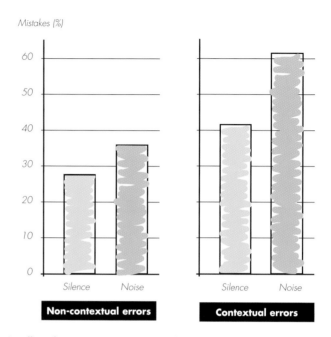

Mistakes (%)

Non-contextual errors

Contextual errors

The effect of noise on concentration and ability to work has been studied at the University of California in the US (Weinstein, 1974). The test group exposed to noise (from a telex machine) worked less regularly and found it more difficult to identify predominantly contextual errors, compared with another group who were able to work in silence.

Both groups were given the task of finding contextual errors (grammatical errors, incorrect word choices, etc.) and non-contextual errors (spelling mistakes, etc.) in a text.

The diagram on the right (which represents a more complicated task) shows larger differences in terms of the results of working in silent and noisy environments respectively compared with the diagram on the left. The columns show average results from the test which was carried out in two batches using college students.

Chronic exposure to aeroplane noise results in increased blood pressure and poorer results in medical tests indicating stress. It also has a negative effect on the long-term memory. This is shown by studies of school children, who also displayed poorer results in standardised reading tests (Evans, Bullinger, Hygge et al, 1995, 1998).

In addition, studies show that noise has a detrimental impact on school results. Noise also has a cumulative effect which becomes more obvious the higher up the school the pupils are, as they have been exposed to noise for a longer period.

The ability to read is affected more by noise than, for example, mathematical skills. Reading skills require dialogue between teacher and pupil, and in this situation noise is a disturbance. Studies also show that the basic mechanisms which affect alertness and factors such as stamina and motivation are adversely affected by constant exposure to noise.

Research shows that **pupils' ability to recite a memorised text is adversely affected** by road traffic noise (during learning) and irrelevant but meaningful speech (you understand what is said, but the speech has nothing to do with the work in question).

After-effects and motivation

When it comes to after-effects (behaviour after the noise has stopped) – it appears that intermittent and chronic **noise has negative consequences, particularly for difficult tasks.** Aircraft noise in particular (occuring suddenly and having significant peaks) causes clear after-effects, which makes teaching next to an airport entirely inappropriate.

Human speech also has a major impact as a source of noise. **Motivation and stamina are adversely affected** by sudden, intermittent noise from speech even at low levels.

When it is noisy we raise our voices. For teachers, for example, good room acoustics where the noise is muted are necessary if they are not to risk damaging their voice. Voice problems are common in today's schools. A quotation from the newspaper "The Straits Times" (Singapore): "...this is a problem faced by many teachers in developed countries... Extensive surveys and research carried out in this area have in recent years revealed that the problem can be attributed to high levels of background noise and the high reverberation times that occur in classrooms."

Noise and social behaviour

A noisy environment makes it more difficult to hear and be heard. This can lead to introversion, irritation and indifference. It also makes it more difficult to exchange feelings and thoughts, which may contribute to a feeling of **isolation and loneliness**. For people with experiences of war and similar crisis situations, noise and sudden sounds can be frightening. Noise is also believed to reduce people's willingness to provide assistance, a particular type of indifference (Korte, Ympa and Toppen, 1975. Korte and Grant, 1980). Noise itself does not appear to cause aggressive behaviour, but this may occur in combination with provocation or pent-up rage and hostility in people (e.g. Jones & Chapman, 1984).

Most people have experience of the way children and adults can easily become rowdy in a noisy environment.

Don't let room acoustics become a stress factor

Noise breeds noise, noisy environments spread aggression and stress and have negative effects on behaviour. Having to spend time in a poor sound environment and not being able to influence it causes stress in itself.

A good sound environment with little opportunity for sound to spread, the correct reverberation time and thus good speech intelligibility is a major step towards reduced "sound stress".

Stress – disturbing the equilibrium

Canadian researcher Hans Selye has described stress as the way the body becomes wound up when a person faces a challenge or a threat. Our body and mind seeks to maintain equilibrium – biochemically, physiologically and psychologically. Stress is a change to this equilibrium. The reasons for the changes are called stressors. Stress is fundamentally a value-neutral concept, i.e. neither good or bad. It is only when the equilibrium is disturbed over a long period that negative effects can arise.

A cold shower, an exciting film or a sportsman warming up before a competition – all these cause appropriate amounts of stress which are accepted by the organism, stimulate it and increase its performance.

"I have such a terrible stomach ache and sometimes headaches. The classroom is so noisy and rowdy, and then there's the stress over grades, I can't cope with it all," Sofia, aged 15.

The use and understanding of language of pre-school children improves if the nursery is equipped with sound-absorbing material which reduces the noise (Maxwell and Evans, USA, 2000).

If, on the other hand, the person is faced with a series of new situations, far more demanding than what he or she is used to and able to tolerate, stress with negative consequences can arise as the equilibrium has been disrupted more than the organism is able to accept. It is therefore important to find a level which is appropriate for each person. This can be difficult in today's society when many people are subject to time pressure and high demands in terms of performance.

Excess or deficiency

Stressors have one thing in common: they mean an excess or deficiency of the influences to which the organism is normally exposed (e.g. heating, air pressure and noise), or influences from something new (e.g. bacteria, a potential accident, etc.). Stressors can also be psychological, such as a poor working situation or a stressful private relationship. A physical stimulus, for example poisoning, can cause both physical and psychological stress. Besides the duration of the stress, its strength and the individual's receptivity (health, lifestyle, etc.) determine whether it causes illness or not.

Preventing stress

To reduce stress and the number of people on sick leave due to "burn-out", for example, it becomes all the more important to prevent stress as society becomes more complex.

A humanitarian view of people combined with healthy economic thinking and responsibility for the environment are cornerstones of work in this respect. By placing "the right person in the right place" stressors such as excessive demands or under-stimulation can be avoided. Long-term staff care which addresses both the physical and the psychosocial working environment is a tool for creating a functioning workplace. For the individual this is about taking responsibility for one's own health and well-being by attempting to balance work and leisure, taking exercise, eating properly and so on.

A serious question of a more theoretical nature is why should people adapt to society? Shouldn't it be the other way round, that society should be adapted to human needs and abilities?

Stress – cause and effect

The endocrine glands and the autonomous nervous system are our body's most important defence mechanism. Researcher Hans Selye terms what happens in both systems in a stressful situation "the general adaptation syndrome". The syndrome contains three main stages:

1) Alarm reaction – when the body and mind is exposed to stress (equilibrium is disrupted), the body quickly mobilises its defences. The autonomous nervous system and the endocrine glands are reset to eliminate the effects of the stress.

Examples of symptoms: Irregular or fast heartbeat, anxiety, muscle cramps primarily in the back, shoulders and neck.

2) Resistance – if the stress is considerable and continues, the body attempts to repair damage caused during the alarm reaction, partly via increased production of adrenocortical hormones (corticosteroids). At this stage a certain amount of adaptation to stress has taken place.

Example of how stress in the resistance stage can be handled in the workplace: Either the situation is resolved by talking about the problem (experienced as being problematic at the time but positive in the long term, a solution which also increases self-confidence) or one sticks one's head in the sand and in the worst cases takes refuge in abuse (provides a short-term release but is destructive over time).

3) Exhaustion – if the stress continues for a long time, there is a risk that one's defences will not be sufficient. In this case the stressors gain the opportunity to cause the same damage as during the alarm reaction and the result is that the body and mind collapses.

Examples of symptoms: muscle cramps, raised blood pressure, impaired immune defences, depression, difficulty concentrating and sudden loss of short-term memory.

Stress in the workplace – some examples:

- Noise
- Temperature too high or too low
- Poor sitting position
- Fear (of punishment)
- Joy (at rewards)
- Anger (at unfair treatment)
- Competition
- Time pressure
- Uncertainty and lack of control
- Lack of support from superiors and colleagues
- Too high demands in terms of performance
- Too low demands in terms of performance, leading to monotony

Model of the effects of direct and indirect noise.

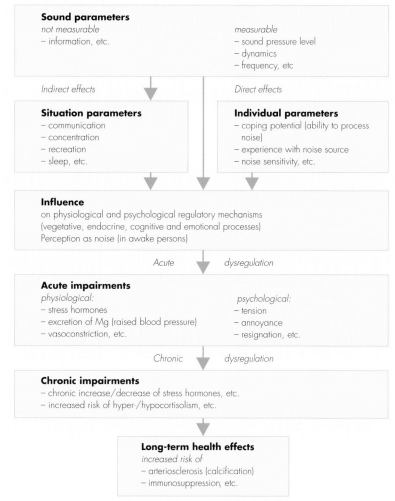

Sound parameters
not measurable
– information, etc.

measurable
– sound pressure level
– dynamics
– frequency, etc

Indirect effects   *Direct effects*

Situation parameters
– communication
– concentration
– recreation
– sleep, etc.

Individual parameters
– coping potential (ability to process noise)
– experience with noise source
– noise sensitivity, etc.

Influence
on physiological and psychological regulatory mechanisms
(vegetative, endocrine, cognitive and emotional processes)
Perception as noise (in awake persons)

Acute   *dysregulation*

Acute impairments
physiological:
– stress hormones
– excretion of Mg (raised blood pressure)
– vasoconstriction, etc.

psychological:
– tension
– annoyance
– resignation, etc.

Chronic   *dysregulation*

Chronic impairments
– chronic increase/decrease of stress hormones, etc.
– increased risk of hyper-/hypocortisolism, etc.

Long-term health effects
increased risk of
– arteriosclerosis (calcification)
– immunosuppression, etc.

(Source: H. Ising and C. Braun, acute and cronic endocrine effects of noise, Noise & Health, 2000)

Poor room acoustics can affect teachers and pupils as follows – some effects worth considering

- Pupils have difficulty hearing what teachers and classmates are saying during lessons.

- Pupils have to concentrate on understanding individual words and may therefore miss the context. Children also work more slowly when noise levels are high and suffer memory problems.

- Younger pupils have limited experience and find it difficult to understand words which are unclear. Pupils are not able to "decode" unclear words until around the age of fifteen.

- Pupils in noisy school environments often have higher blood pressure and a faster heart rate than others. This can cause damage in the long term. Raised levels of stress hormones are also found in both pupils and teachers.

- Many pupils close themselves off socially and have problems benefiting from teaching or finding friends and they can be seen as less intelligent and rowdy. There is a clear link between noise and rowdy behaviour.

- "Poor hearing is invisible", which makes it difficult to identify those affected.

- Teachers suffer from poorer health when they are forced to strain their voices. The risk that they may have to visit a doctor for damage to the vocal chords, for example, increases considerably, often resulting in long periods of sick leave.

- It is said that noise leads to more noise. This means that a classroom with poor acoustics to begin with gains an even worse sound environment when pupils and staff have to use their vocal resources to a great extent. Students and teachers feel much better under acceptable acoustic conditions.

- At nurseries and pre-schools the noise often reaches 80 dB(A) and over. Chronic exposure to noise during the child's early years can damage the child's ability to learn the language, for example.

- Pupils with the slightest hearing impairment suffer more from poor room acoustics. Often the impaired hearing associated with having a cold is enough for a major drop in speech intelligibility to occur.

How the central nervous system and intellectual work are affected by sound/noise:

- We react instinctively to sound and are easily distracted if the sound heard has nothing to do with the work we are doing. A few seconds' distraction can result in us missing information or losing the thread of our thinking.

- Sensory impressions activate us up to a certain level. If we receive too many, or the wrong sensory impressions, these suddenly become disturbing. The point at which we become disturbed varies from person to person.

- Monotonous repetitive tasks can be made easier by certain types of background noise.

- Difficult tasks which require concentration on the other hand are not made easier by background noise. On the contrary, performance worsens!

- "Tunnel vision" in the hearing system: a noisy environment can force people to shut themselves off (mentally disconnect) from verbal/acoustic information. The problem is that we easily miss important information.

- In a noisy environment we can be so disturbed that we do not have the energy to choose between several strategies for accomplishing a task. Instead we choose "the easy way out" and maybe do a worse job.

- We do not achieve our best in a noisy environment. Coping with the noise is a job in itself. We become tense and try to mentally distance ourselves from the noise. This means we do not have sufficient energy to put everything we have into the task at hand.

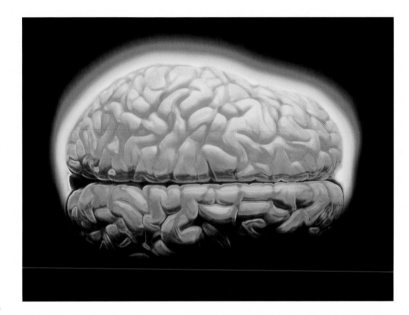

- Noise also leaves us tired. We often perform worse after exposure to noise than during it, resulting in tiredness, irritation and depression.

- Noise masks speech. In a noisy environment it is difficult for speech to reach the listener. We have to put more effort into speaking and listening, which is not made any easier by having tasks to perform at the same time, e.g. during a lesson.

Some international studies of noise in learning environments

Canada: "... many teachers considered noise to be detrimental to their work, in particular interfering with speech. Noise in an educational setting has many detrimental effects that may have significant psychological and physical impacts on both children and teachers. Noise problems may be even more acute for people with special problems, be they perceptual, socio-emotional or cognitive." (Teachers at six schools interviewed about noise. Hétu, Truchon, Gagnon, Bilodeau. 1990)

US: School children suffering from noise stress are more difficult to motivate and they give up more easily when tasks become more difficult. (Evans. 1998)

US: When acoustical improvements were carried out, the children were able to improve their performance in early reading, learning numbers and their speech ability. (Nurseries investigated, Maxwell, Evans. 1988)

UK: "These long reverberation times and high background noise levels create poor speech intelligibility in most classrooms and this has been verified by objective and subjective measurements. These facts confirm that poor acoustics can be harmful to a good learning environment. [...] Another result of poor acoustics, particularly noisy classrooms, is that staff are more likely to take days off sick and suffer voice and throat problems. This could well lead to increased costs and disruption to the children's education as supply teachers are brought in." (MacKenzie, Airey. 1999)

Finland: Voice disorders of teachers in day centres for children were mainly caused by inadequate acoustics in the rooms and by the necessity to speak more loudly than normal over long periods. (Sala, Airo, Lain, Olkinuora, Pentti, Suonpää. 1998)

Germany: Hearing-impaired children (aged 7 – 12) found it more difficult to discriminate between spoken words when the "speech noise" around them increased. (Geffner, Lucker, Koch. 1996)

Belarus: Sound levels of over 75 dB(A) were measured in the recess halls in school centres in Belarus containing between 1,800 and 2,200 students, making it impossible for them to relax. (Kryukova, Abramchuk. 1991)

China: Without exception pupils perform better in quiet classrooms. The cognitive capabilities of primary school children were studied in classrooms with noise levels ranging from 42 dB(A) to 55 dB(A) and over. (Niu. 1990)

Points to remember:

- In learning situations the spoken word is the most important.

- The quality of education is higher when listeners can hear well.

- Speech lies within the frequency range 125 – 8,000 Hz.

- Sound is energy and is caused when particles in a medium, e.g. air, are set moving.

- Echo is a major problem in indoor environments.

- Reverberation time is the time it takes from a source of sound being turned off until its sound pressure level has fallen by 60 dB.

- Speech intelligibility is affected by reverberation time, the shape of the room, the relationship between speech and background noise and the listener's hearing. RASTI, STI and %ALcons are some common ways of measuring speech intelligibility.

- An absorber reduces the echo effect and noise level.

- Corti's organ contains the sensory cells where the sound sensation begins to take shape.

- Humans, discern sound in the frequency range 20 – 20,000 Hz.

- The ears' hair cells have to be able to rest, otherwise there is a risk that they will be damaged and hearing impaired.

- Good room acoustics create security.

- People with impaired hearing are disturbed more by background noise than those with normal hearing.

- Understanding a foreign language in a room with the wrong acoustics is considerably more demanding than understanding one's mother tongue.

- The common cold reduces hearing.

- Noise is "unwanted sound".

- Noise affects attention, memory, ability to solve problems and decision-making.

References – Sound in the learning environment

Airey, Sharon (2000). *Education*. Paper/Airey. (in English)

Andersson, Johnny (1998). *Akustik & buller: en praktisk handbok (Acoustics and noise – a practical handbook)*. AB Svensk Byggtjänst. (in Swedish)

Berglund, Birgitta & Lindvall, Thomas (edited by) (1995). *Community Noise*. Stockholm University and Karolinska Institute/World Health Organization, Archives of the Center for Sensory Research, Volume 2, Issue 1, 1995. (in English)

Bilsom, (now Dalloz Safety) (1981). *När, var och hur vi hör (When, where and how we hear)*. Brochure/Dalloz Safety. (in Swedish)

Crandell, C. Carl (1993). *Speech Recognition in Noise by Children with Minimal Degrees of Sensorineural Hearing Loss*. Ear & Hearing, Vol. 14, No. 3, 1993. (in English)

Ecophon (1998). *Ljud och det moderna kontoret (Sound and the Modern Office)*. Ecophon. (in Swedish, English, Dutch, French, German, Danish, Polish)

Evans, Gary W. & Bullinger, Monika & Hygge, Staffan (1995). *Chronic noise and psychological stress*. Psychological Science, Vol. 6, No. 6, Nov 1995. (in English)

Evans, Gary W. & Bullinger, Monika & Hygge, Staffan (1998). *Chronic noise exposure and psychological response: A prospective study of children living under environmental stress*. Psychological Science, Vol. 9, No. 1, Jan 1998. (in English)

Harris, Sten (interview with audiology specialist Dr Harris, associate professor and head of department at Lund University Hospital, Sweden, 1995)

Hellström, Björn (1999). *Akustisk design vad är det? (What is acoustic design?)* Bygg & Teknik, 3/99. (in Swedish)

Ising, H & Braun, C. (2000). *Acute and chronic endocrine effects of noise: Review of the research conducted at the Institute for Water, Soil and Air Hygiene*. Noise & Health 2000;7,7-24. (in English)

Kjellberg, Anders et al (1993). Forskning & Praktik 4/1993. (in Swedish)

Kjellberg, Anders (1990). *Inte bara hörselskador (Not only hearing impairment)*. Arbetslivsinstitutet (National Institute for Working Life), 1990:36. (in Swedish)

Landström, Ulf & Arlinger, Stig & Hygge, Staffan & Johansson, Örjan & Kjellberg, Anders & Persson Waye, Kerstin (1999). *Störande buller: Kunskapsöversikt för kriteriedokumentation (Disturbing noise: Survey of criteria documentation)*. Arbetslivsinstitutet (National Institute for Working Life), 1999:27. (in Swedish)

Lerner, Thomas (2000). *Skolan stressar eleverna (School makes students stressed)*. Dagens Nyheter 2000-02-24. (in Swedish)

Luthman, Gösta et al (ed.) (1969). *Handbok i ergonomi (Handbook on ergonomics)*. Almqvist & Wiksell. (in Swedish)

Mackenzie, David J. & Airey, Sharon (1999). *Classroom acoustics – a research project: Summary report*. Heriot-Watt University, Edinburgh, Scotland. (in English)

Maxwell, Lorraine E. & Evans, Gary W. (2000). *The effects of noise on pre-school children's pre-reading skills*. Journal of Environmental Psychology, 2000, 20, 91-97. (in English)

Nabelek AK & Donahue AM (1984). *Perceptions of consonants in reverberation by native and non-native listeners*. Journal of the Acoustical Society of America, 75, 632-34, 1984. (in English)

Nationalencyklopedin (Swedish National Encyclopedia) (1998-). Bra Böcker. (in Swedish)

Norinder, Eva (interview with Eva Norinder, teacher of the hearing-impaired, Göteborg, Sweden, 1999)

Onciul, Julia von (1996). *ABC of Work Related Disorders: Stress at work*. British Medical Journal, 1996;313:745-748 (21 Sept). (in English)

Royal Institute for the Deaf and Hard of Hearing

Ruhe, Carsten (2000). *Kommunikationsräume*. Paper/Ruhe. (in German)

Schick, August & Meis, Markus & Reckhardt, Carsten (edited by) (2000). *Contributions to Psychological Acoustics; Results of the eighth Oldenburg symposium on psychological acoustics*. Bibliotheks- und Informationssystem der Universität Oldenburg. (in English)

Synskadades Riksförbund (The Swedish Association of the Visually Impaired)

Weinstein, Neil D. (1974). *Effect of noise on intellectual performance*. Journal of Applied Psychology, 1974, Vol. 59, No. 5, 548-554. (in English)

Yap Sau Hee (1999). *Good acoustics will help teachers*. The Straits Times (Singapore), December 18, 1999. (in English)

Glossary

A sound which some people feel is pleasant music may be perceived as noise by others.

Acoustics

The study of sound. In everyday language also refers to how sound is experienced in particular premises.

Articulation Index, AI

The Articulation Index (AI) objectively measures speech intelligibility in a multi-step process. The spectrum of sound pressure levels in a room is compared with a reference spectrum from an echo-free room. Correction is made for certain parameters, e.g. reverberation time, so that the comparison is relevant.

Articulation Loss of Consonants, %ALcons

One method of objectively measuring speech intelligibility is Articulation Loss of Consonants (%ALcons), the number of consonants missed shown as a percentage. Consonants play a considerably more important role in speech intelligibility than vowels. If you hear the consonants well, you can understand the speech well.

Noise

Unwanted sound. Noise can often be an individual experience of a particular sound, e.g. a background noise.

Background noise

E.g. speech, scraping chairs, humming ventilation, traffic noise, noise from machinery and equipment, sound from corridors, adjoining rooms and the playground.

Reverberation time (T or RT)

The time it takes for the sound pressure level to fall by 60 dB after the sound has been turned off. Measuring the reverberation time allows us to calculate the total sound absorption. The reverberation time varies according to the frequency. The recommendations for reverberation time in this book refer to frequencies between 125 and 4,000 Hz.

Flutter echo

Occurs when noise bounces between parallel surfaces or of a corner of a room.

Frequency (f)

Stated in Hz (hertz). The higher the value, the lighter the tone (treble – bass). The frequency of speech primarily lies between 125 and 8,000 Hz, while audible sound lies between 20 and 20,000 Hz.

Sound absorption

Sound energy is converted into mechanical vibration energy and/or heat energy.

Sound absorbers

Materials and structures with the ability to "suck up" sound energy and convert it to other forms of energy. They improve room acoustics by removing sound reflections, so reducing the noise and the reverberation time.

Sound pressure/sound pressure level (dB)

The variations caused by sound waves in air are called sound pressure. The lowest sound pressure level which can be heard is 0 dB, known as the hearing threshold. The highest level which can be tolerated is called the pain threshold and is around 120 dB.

Sound strength (dB)

Measured in dB (deciBel). dB are measured at different frequencies. dB(A) (now also L_{pA}) is a single-figure value used to describe the total sound strength for all frequencies in a way similar to the sensitivity of the ear. dB(C) (now also L_{pC}) particularly focuses on low frequencies and better reflects how a sound is experienced by people with impaired hearing.

RASTI

RASTI (RApid Speech Transmission Index) is an objective way of measuring speech intelligibility. Speech intelligibility is measured at two frequencies, 500 and 2,000 Hz, by placing a loudspeaker which transmits sound from the location of the person speaking and a microphone where the listeners are sitting.

Speech Transmission Index, STI

Similar to the RASTI method but a more complete form of measuring speech intelligibility by measuring all octave bands in the frequency range 125 – 8,000 Hz.

Speech intelligibility

Speech intelligibility is directly dependent on the level of background noise, reverberation time and the shape of the room. In a normal classroom the requirement for good speech intelligibility is a RASTI-value of at least 0.75. This can be achieved if the background noise is a maximum of 30 dB(A) (now also L_{pA}) and 45 dB(C) (now also L_{pC}) and the reverberation time does not exceed 0.5 seconds.

Good room acoustics are required in every indoor environment where people work and socialise.

Advice on room acoustics in educational premises

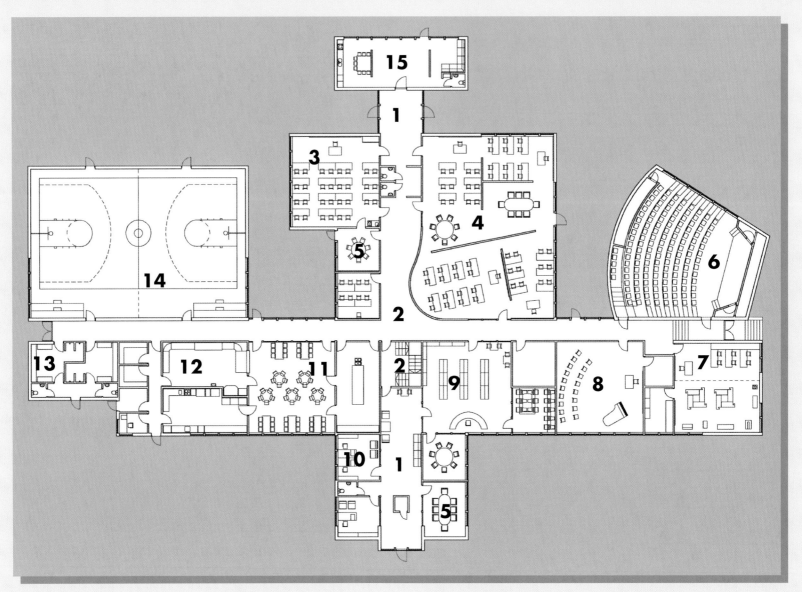

1 Entrances/Communal areas/
Cloakrooms

2 Corridors/Stairs

3 Classrooms (< 100 m²)

4 Open-plan teaching environments

5 Conference rooms/Group study
rooms (< 100 m²)

6 Lecture theatres/Assembly halls/
Auditoriums

7 Workshops

8 Music rooms/Drama rooms/
Dance rooms

9 Libraries/Multi-media resource
centres/Study rooms/Staffrooms

10 Offices/Receptions

11 Canteens/Cafeterias/Restaurants

12 Kitchens

13 Changing rooms/Showers

14 Gymnasiums/Swimming pools/
Sports halls (< 1500 m³)

15 Play and activity rooms

What type of sound is generated in a teaching environment? What reverberation time is recommended? This chapter contains a whole host of advice and recommendations regarding acoustics in a number of common types of room. The purpose of this summary is to facilitate the planning process.

This chapter defines various activities and the sound problems associated with the premises in which they occur. It also shows the recommendations made by the authorities, which in this case refer to UK Guidelines Building Bulletin 87 (BB87), Guidelines for Environmental Design in Schools, part A/BB93 and Swedish Standard SS 02 52 68 (Acoustics – Sound classification of spaces in buildings – Institutional premises, rooms for education, day care centres and after school centres, rooms for office work and hotels). These standards give instructions on requirements for:

• Airborne sound insulation
• Impact sound insulation
• Room acoustics
• Noise from installations
• Traffic noise

Although the following recommendations only show the figures for room acoustics, it is naturally important to adhere to all the other acoustic parameters.

Ecophon's recommendations are based on more than 30 years' experience in the field, as well as UK and international research.

In general, planning using high standards for sound is recommended, as this makes life easier for everyone, particularly people with impaired vision or hearing. In addition, it is rarely the case that higher sound standards cost more in terms of room acoustics.

It is also a good idea to achieve "uniformity in room acoustics", i.e. approximately the same reverberation time in all spaces where students and staff spend their time. Variations in room acoustics affect behaviour. People lower their voices in rooms with short reverberation times and raise them in rooms with long reverberation times.

Entrances/Communal areas/Cloakrooms

These areas function as transport routes, meeting places and break areas where people come and go and where a great deal of verbal communication takes place. They are natural gathering points. They are also a place to enjoy social contact and to relax between lessons.

- Large open areas encourage conversation at a distance, which results in people tending to raise their voices and trying to be heard over others. Sound breeds sound, creating a disturbing "cocktail of noise".

- Music may also contribute to the noise level.

- Hard surface materials reflect sound, which creates problematic sound amplification and sound propagation. The sound is transported a long way and so disturbs a large number of people.

- Hard flooring creates noisy footsteps.

The authorities' recommendation

No recommendations in the UK Guidelines for these areas, contained within Building Bulletin 87 (BB87), Guidelines for Environmental Design in Schools, Part A.

Note: please also refer to Building Bulletin 93, which will replace Part A of Building Bulletin 87.

Swedish Standard 02 52 68 recommends a reverberation time of 0.5 or 0.6 seconds depending on the selected quality level for the communal area. This applies to normally furnished rooms but unoccupied. The above figure is the highest recommended value for the frequency range 250 – 4,000 Hz. At 125 Hz a value 20% higher is permitted.

Ecophon's recommendation

We recommend a reverberation time of 0.5 seconds. According to the Swedish standard, to achieve this a full acoustic ceiling is needed of sound absorption class A (in accordance with EN ISO 11654).

Bearing in mind the risk of damage, the acoustic ceiling may need an impact resistant surface layer.

The entrance provides a visitor's first impression of the building. It can therefore be important to convey architectural values through features such as a multi-level ceiling with built-in lighting.

Corridors/Stairs

Corridors and stairs are frequently visited areas. People come and go in a steady stream. These areas also act as transport routes for people and for objects.

- Open areas encourage conversation at a distance, which results in people tending to raise their voices and trying to be heard over others. Sound breeds sound, creating a disturbing "cocktail of noise".

- Hard surface materials create problematic sound amplification and sound propagation. The sound is transported a long way and so disturbs a large number of people in adjacent classrooms.

- Hard flooring creates noisy footsteps.

- Parallel walls can create problematic flutter echoes.

The authorities' recommendation

No recommendations in the UK Guidelines for these areas, contained within Building Bulletin 87 (BB87), Guidelines for Environmental Design in Schools, Part A.

Note: please also refer to Building Bulletin 93, which will replace Part A of Building Bulletin 87.

Swedish Standard 02 52 68 recommends a reverberation time of 0.6 or 0.8 seconds in corridors, and 0.8 or 1.0 seconds for stairs, depending on the selected quality level. This applies to normally furnished but unoccupied spaces. The above figure is the highest recommended value for the frequency range 250 – 4,000 Hz. At 125 Hz a value 20% higher is permitted.

Ecophon's recommendation

For corridors we recommend a reverberation time of 0.6 seconds. According to the Swedish standard, to achieve this a full acoustic ceiling is needed of sound absorption class B (in accordance with EN ISO 11654).

For stairs we recommend 0.8 seconds. According to the above Swedish standard, to achieve this an acoustic ceiling of sound absorption class A (in accordance with EN ISO 11654) covering 60% of the ceiling surface is needed.

In practice, this means covering the underside of the landing.

Bearing in mind the risk of damage, the acoustic ceiling may need an impact resistant surface layer.

Corridors often have a large number of installations above the acoustic ceiling. As access to these is frequently required, it may be a good idea to select a demountable acoustic ceiling.

Nowadays the focus is on utilising all parts of a school for education. Equally high standards should therefore be applied to corridors, etc. as to other teaching spaces.

Classrooms (<100 m²)

Classrooms are the most common type of room in a school building and the location for not only desk-bound teaching, but group work and individual study. Hearing and seeing well is crucial to the learning process and good speech intelligibility is a must. The room has to promote intellectual work and concentration.

- Hard surface materials create problematic sound reflections which limit speech intelligibility.

- Hard flooring creates noisy footsteps and scraping noises from chairs and tables.

The authorities' recommendation

UK Guidelines, BB87, Part A, recommend that in both primary and secondary schools an unoccupied mid-frequency reverberation time of between 0.5 – 0.8 seconds be achieved for children with normal hearing. Approximate size for primary school classroom, area 30 – 65 m², and height 2.4 – 3.0 m. Approximate size for secondary school classroom, area 50 – 70 m², and height 2.4 – 3.0 m. For teaching the hearing impaired it is recommended an unoccupied mid-frequency reverberation time of between 0.3 – 0.6 seconds be achieved.

Note: please also refer to Building Bulletin 93, which will replace Part A of Building Bulletin 87.

Swedish Standard 02 52 68 recommends a reverberation time of 0.5 or 0.6 seconds, depending on the selected quality level. This applies to normally furnished but unoccupied rooms. The above figure is the highest recommended value for the frequency range 250 – 4,000 Hz. At 125 Hz a value 20% higher is permitted.

Ecophon's recommendation

We recommend a reverberation time of 0.5 seconds or less. According to the above Swedish standard, to achieve this an acoustic ceiling of sound absorption class A (in accordance with EN ISO 11654) covering 85% of the ceiling surface is needed. The rear wall should also be fitted with a wall absorber of sound absorption class A. Increased absorption at 125 Hz may be required, particularly for listeners and speakers with impaired sight or hearing.

For good speaker comfort, add a reflector over the teacher's desk area.

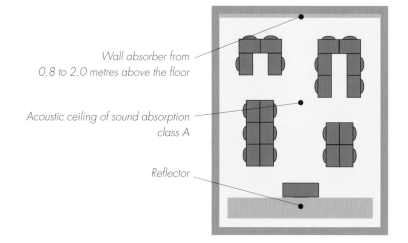

Wall absorber from 0.8 to 2.0 metres above the floor

Acoustic ceiling of sound absorption class A

Reflector

Open-plan teaching environments

Modern teaching is seeing new pedagogical and more cost-effective methods of exploiting teaching time and premises. An open-plan teaching environment has several groups of students sharing one or more teachers. This means many people working in the same area. The method is similar to working in an open-plan office.

■ The open area may encourage conversation at a distance, while at the same time people move around the whole area, which creates disturbing noise.

■ Hard surface materials create problematic sound amplification and sound propagation. The sound is transported a long way and so disturbs a large number of people.

■ Hard flooring creates noisy footsteps.

The authorities' recommendation

UK Guidelines, BB87, Part A, for primary and secondary schools, states, "To realise the limited acoustic potential of open plan areas, a carpeted floor is recommended together with an acoustically absorbent ceiling. In addition acoustically absorbent screens, of typical height 1.7 m, should be interposed between class groups."

Note: please also refer to Building Bulletin 93, which will replace Part A of Building Bulletin 87.

Swedish Standard 02 52 68 recommends a reverberation time of 0.4 seconds. This applies to normally furnished but unoccupied rooms. The above figure is the highest recommended value for the frequency range 250 – 4,000 Hz. At 125 Hz a value 20% higher is permitted.

Ecophon's recommendation

We recommend a reverberation time of 0.4 seconds. According to the Swedish standard, to achieve this a full acoustic ceiling is needed of sound absorption class A (in accordance with EN ISO 11654).

Certain wall surfaces may need to be fitted with sound absorbers.

This type of teaching environment is difficult to master with regard to sound. It is, therefore, a good idea to carry out a serious analysis of the pros and cons before planning.

Conference rooms/Group study rooms (<100 m²)

In this type of room people usually work in groups gathered around a table. Verbal communication takes place in all parts of the room, which makes speech intelligibility vital throughout the room.

- Hard surface materials create problematic sound reflections which impede speech intelligibility.

- Hard flooring creates noisy footsteps and scraping noises from chairs and tables.

The authorities' recommendation

UK Guidelines, BB87, Part A, recommend that in secondary schools an unoccupied mid-frequency reverberation time of between 0.4 – 0.8 seconds be achieved for children with normal hearing, approximate size, area 6 – 10 m², and height 2.7 – 3.0 m.

There are no recommendations for this area in primary schools or for the hearing impaired in Building Bulletin 87.

Note: please also refer to Building Bulletin 93, which will replace Part A of Building Bulletin 87.

Swedish Standard 02 52 68 recommends a reverberation time of 0.5 or 0.6 seconds, depending on the selected quality level. This applies to normally furnished but unoccupied rooms. The above figure is the highest recommended value for the frequency range 250 – 4,000 Hz. At 125 Hz a value 20% higher is permitted.

Ecophon's recommendation

We recommend a reverberation time of 0.5 seconds. According to the Swedish standard, to achieve this a full acoustic ceiling is needed of sound absorption class B (in accordance with EN ISO 11654).

If the room is larger than 100 m², reflectors may be necessary in the central part of the ceiling.

Lecture theatres/Assembly halls/Auditoriums

These rooms are used for lectures and exams, two areas of use which are difficult to reconcile from the point of view of room acoustics. A lecture requires good speech intelligibility, while an exam needs sound to be suppressed in order for people to concentrate. If the room is also used for music and theatre performances, planning the acoustics becomes complicated.

■ As it is impossible to optimise the room for each purpose, it is important to carry out a broad use analysis. Decide what the room will mainly be used for and plan for that purpose.

The authorities' recommendation
UK Guidelines, BB87, Part A, recommend that in primary schools an unoccupied mid-frequency reverberation time of between 0.8 – 1.2 seconds be achieved for children with normal hearing, approximate size, area 80 – 200 m², and height 3.7 – 6.0 m. It is recommended in secondary schools an unoccupied mid-frequency reverberation time of between 1.0 – 1.4 seconds be achieved. Approximate size, area 250 – 550 m², and

height 3.7 – 7.6 m. There are no recommendations for hearing impaired children for these areas in BB87, Part A.

Note: please also refer to Building Bulletin 93, which will replace Part A of Building Bulletin 87.

No Swedish Standard.

Ecophon's recommendation
Refer to an acoustic consultant.

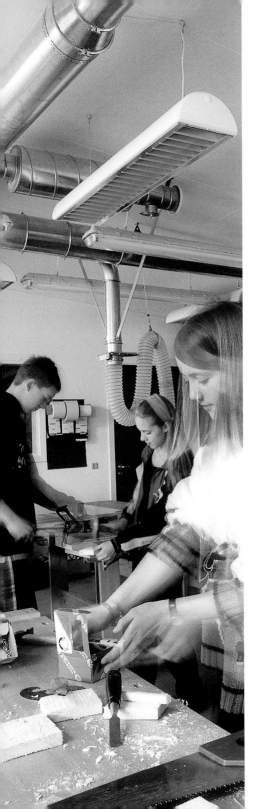

Workshops

Workshops for primarily woodwork and metalwork are the site of noisy work and potentially dangerous machines and tools. The work requires great concentration and is difficult to monitor, so speech intelligibility and safety aspects are crucial.

■ Hard surface materials create problematic sound reflections which impede speech intelligibility to the extent that instructions and warnings may not be heard.

■ Hard flooring creates noisy footsteps.

■ Hard surface materials create problematic sound amplification and sound propagation. The sound is transported a long way and so disturbs a large number of people.

■ This type of space should not be located near quiet activities.

The authorities' recommendation

UK Guidelines, BB87, Part A, recommend that in secondary schools an unoccupied mid-frequency reverberation time of between 0.5 – 0.8 seconds be achieved for children with normal hearing, approximate size, area 80 – 135 m², and height 2.7 – 3.0

m. There are no recommendations for primary schools and hearing impaired children for these areas in BB87, Part A.

Note: please also refer to Building Bulletin 93, which will replace Part A of Building Bulletin 87.

Swedish Standard 02 52 68 recommends a reverberation time of 0.4 or 0.5 seconds depending on the selected quality level. This applies to normally furnished but unoccupied rooms. The above figure is the highest recommended value for the frequency range 250 – 4,000 Hz. At 125 Hz a value 20% higher is permitted.

Ecophon's recommendation

We recommend a reverberation time of 0.4 seconds. According to the Swedish standard, to achieve this a full acoustic ceiling is needed of sound absorption class A (in accordance with EN ISO 11654).

Certain wall surfaces may need to be fitted with sound absorbers.

Bearing in mind the risk of damage, the acoustic ceiling may need an impact resistant surface layer.

Music rooms/Drama rooms/Dance rooms

Rooms designed for music teaching vary a great deal, with students practising singing and music with acoustic and electrically amplified musical instruments. Dance teaching is often a matter of large open spaces and musical accompaniment. In drama teaching the spoken word is vital – it has to be easy to speak and to listen.

■ As it is impossible to optimise the room for each purpose, it is important to carry out a broad use analysis. Decide what the room will mainly be used for and plan for that purpose.

■ This type of space should not be located near quiet activities.

The authorities' recommendation

UK Guidelines, BB87, Part A, recommend that in primary schools an unoccupied mid-frequency reverberation time of between 0.8 – 1.2 seconds be achieved for children with normal hearing, approximate size, area 30 – 80 m², and height 2.4 – 4.0 m. For secondary schools it recommends an unoccupied mid-frequency reverberation time of between 1.0 – 1.2 seconds be achieved. Approxi-

mate size, area 54 – 91 m², and height 2.7 – 3.5 m. There are no recommendations for hearing impaired children for these areas in BB87, Part A.

Also please refer to Building Bulletin 86, Music accommodation in secondary schools – A Design Guide.

Note: please also refer to Building Bulletin 93, which will replace Part A of Building Bulletin 87.

No Swedish Standard.

Ecophon's recommendation

Refer to an acoustic consultant.

Libraries/Multi-media resource centres/ Study rooms/Staffrooms

These areas are the oases of a teaching establishment, allowing self-study and relaxation between lessons. High priority is given to being able to concentrate in a quiet environment.

- The open area may encourage conversation at a distance, while at the same time there are people moving around the whole area and going in and out, which creates disturbing noise.

- Hard surface materials create problematic sound amplification and sound propagation. The sound is transported a long way and so disturbs a large number of people.

- Hard flooring creates noisy footsteps and scraping noises from chairs and tables.

The authorities' recommendation

UK Guidelines, BB87, Part A, recommend that in primary schools an unoccupied mid-frequency reverberation time of between 0.5 – 0.8 seconds be achieved for children with normal hearing, approximate size, area 12 – 70 m², and height 2.4 – 3.0 m. For secondary schools it recommends an unoccupied mid-frequency reverberation time of between 0.5 – 1.0 second be achieved. Approximate size, area 90 – 300 m², and height 2.4 – 3.0 m. There are no recommendations for hearing impaired children for these areas in BB87, Part A.

Note: please also refer to Building Bulletin 93, which will replace Part A of Building Bulletin 87.

Swedish Standard 02 52 68 recommends a reverberation time of 0.5 or 0.6 seconds depending on the selected quality level. This applies to normally furnished but unoccupied rooms. The above figure is the highest recommended value for the frequency range 250 – 4,000 Hz. At 125 Hz a value 20% higher is permitted.

Ecophon's recommendation

We recommend a reverberation time of 0.5 seconds. According to the Swedish standard, to achieve this a full acoustic ceiling is needed of sound absorption class A (in accordance with EN ISO 11654).

Offices/Receptions

All types of teaching establishment have administrative offices, where staff must be able to remain focused and undisturbed, allowing creative thought processes and confidential conversations. The reception is the heart of the establishment, receiving a number of visitors and performing a wide variety of work.

- Hard surface materials create problematic sound reflections which impede speech intelligibility.

- Hard flooring creates noisy footsteps and scraping noises from chairs and tables.

The authorities' recommendation

No recommendations in the UK Guidelines for these areas, contained within Building Bulletin 87 (BB87), Guidelines for Environmental Design in Schools, Part A.

Note: please also refer to Building Bulletin 93, which will replace Part A of Building Bulletin 87.

Swedish Standard 02 52 68 recommends a reverberation time of 0.6 or 0.8 seconds, depending on the selected quality level. This applies to normally furnished but unoccupied rooms. The above figure is the highest recommended value for the frequency range 250 – 4,000 Hz. At 125 Hz a value 20% higher is permitted.

Ecophon's recommendation

We recommend a reverberation time of 0.6 seconds. According to the Swedish standard, to achieve this a full acoustic ceiling is needed of sound absorption class C (in accordance with EN ISO 11654).

Canteens/Cafeterias/Restaurants

It is common for a school to offer its students breakfast or lunch. Many teaching establishments also have a cafeteria or restaurant. This is where students get time to be with their friends and to relax and enjoy social contact.

- Open areas encourage conversation at a distance, which results in people tending to raise their voices and trying to be heard over others. Sound breeds sound, creating a disturbing "cocktail of noise".

- Hard surface materials create problematic sound amplification and sound propagation. The sound is transported a long way and so disturbs a large number of people.

- Hard flooring creates noisy footsteps and scraping noises from chairs and tables.

The authorities' recommendation

UK Guidelines, BB87, Part A, recommend that in primary schools an unoccupied mid-frequency reverberation time of between 0.5 – 0.8 seconds be achieved for children with normal hearing, approximate size, area 80 – 200 m², and height 2.4 – 3.2 m. For secondary schools it recommends an unoccupied mid-frequency reverberation time of between 0.5 – 0.8 seconds be achieved. Approximate size, area 250 – 550 m² and height 3.7 – 7.6 m. There are no recommendations for hearing impaired children for these areas in BB87, Part A.

Note: please also refer to Building Bulletin 93, which will replace Part A of Building Bulletin 87.

Swedish Standard 02 52 68 recommends a reverberation time of 0.5 or 0.6 seconds, depending on the selected quality level. This applies to normally furnished but unoccupied rooms. The above figure is the highest recommended value for the frequency range 250 – 4,000 Hz. At 125 Hz a value 20% higher is permitted.

Ecophon's recommendation

We recommend a reverberation time of 0.5 seconds. According to the Swedish standard, to achieve this a full acoustic ceiling is needed of sound absorption class A (in accordance with EN ISO 11654).

Kitchens

Cooking and washing up are noisy activities. In addition to the sound produced by staff, there is also the noise from catering machinery and extractor fans.

- Hard surface materials create problematic sound amplification and sound propagation. The sound is transported a long way and so disturbs a large number of people.

- Hard flooring creates noisy footsteps.

The authorities' recommendation

UK Guidelines, BB87, Part A, recommend that in primary schools an unoccupied mid-frequency reverberation time of 1.5 seconds be achieved for children with normal hearing, approximate size, area 65 – 120 m², and height 2.7 – 4.0 m. There are no recommendations for secondary schools and the hearing impaired.

Note: please also refer to Building Bulletin 93, which will replace Part A of Building Bulletin 87.

Swedish Standard 02 52 68 recommends a reverberation time of 0.5 or 0.6 seconds, depending on the selected quality level. This applies to normally furnished but unoccupied rooms. The above figure is the highest recommended value for the frequency range 250 – 4,000 Hz. At 125 Hz a value 20% higher is permitted.

Ecophon's recommendation

We recommend a reverberation time of 0.5 seconds. According to the Swedish standard, to achieve this a full acoustic ceiling is needed of sound absorption class A (in accordance with EN ISO 11654).

In view of hygiene requirements, the acoustic ceiling must not attract dirt and must be washable.

It will also have to tolerate relatively high levels of humidity.

Changing rooms/Showers

Changing rooms and showers are often a meeting point before and after sports activities where the atmosphere and noise level can be very high.

- Open areas encourage conversation at a distance, which results in people tending to raise their voices and trying to be heard over others. Sound breeds sound, creating a disturbing "cocktail of noise".

- Hard surface materials create problematic sound amplification and sound propagation. The sound is transported a long way and so disturbs a large number of people.

- Hard flooring creates noisy footsteps.

The authorities' recommendation

No recommendations in the UK Guidelines for these areas, contained within Building Bulletin 87 (BB87), Guidelines for Environmental Design in Schools, Part A.

Note: please also refer to Building Bulletin 93, which will replace Part A of Building Bulletin 87.

Swedish Standard 02 52 68 recommends a reverberation time of 0.6 or 0.8 seconds, depending on the selected quality level for the changing rooms. This applies to normally furnished but unoccupied rooms. The above figure is the highest recommended value for the frequency range 250 – 4,000 Hz. At 125 Hz a value 20% higher is permitted.

Ecophon's recommendation

We recommend a reverberation time of 0.6 seconds. According to the above Swedish standard, to achieve this a full acoustic ceiling is needed of sound absorption class B (in accordance with EN ISO 11654).

The acoustic ceiling will also have to tolerate relatively high levels of humidity.

Girls' school washroom from bygone age.

Gymnasiums/Swimming pools/Sports halls (<1500 m³)

Physical training, ball games, swimming and water games are associated with very high sound levels. It is important to be able to communicate – instructions must be able to be given and heard. Naturally, consideration must also be given to safety aspects when designing the right sound environment in these spaces.

■ Large open areas encourage conversation at a distance, which results in people tending to raise their voices and trying to be heard over others. Sound breeds sound, creating a disturbing "cocktail of noise".

■ Hard surface materials create problematic sound amplification and sound propagation. The sound is transported a long way and so disturbs a large number of people.

■ Hard flooring creates noisy footsteps.

The authorities' recommendation

UK Guidelines, BB87, Part A, recommend that in primary schools in gymnasiums an unoccupied mid-frequency reverberation time of between 0.8 – 1.2 seconds be achieved for children with normal hearing, approximate size, area 80 – 200 m², and height 3.7 – 6.0 m. For secondary schools, in gymnasiums it recommends an unoccupied mid-frequency reverberation time of between 1.0 – 1.5 seconds be achieved. Approximate size, area 250 – 550 m² and height 5.0 – 6.0 m.

For swimming pools in primary schools it recommends that an unoccupied mid-frequency reverberation time of less than 2.0 seconds be achieved, approximate size, area 65 – 120 m², and height 3.7 – 6.0 m.

For swimming pools in secondary schools it recommends that an unoccupied mid-frequency reverberation time of less than 2.0 seconds be achieved. Approximate size, area 100 – 500 m², and height 3.0 – 6.0 m. There are no recommendations for hearing impaired children for these areas in BB87, Part A.

Swedish Standard 02 52 68 recommends a reverberation time of 1.0 or

1.2 seconds, depending on the selected quality level. This applies to normally furnished but unoccupied rooms. The above figure is the highest recommended value for the frequency range 250 – 4,000 Hz. At 125 Hz a value 20% higher is permitted.

Ecophon's recommendation

We recommend a reverberation time of 1.0 seconds. According to the above Swedish standard, to achieve this a full acoustic ceiling is needed of sound absorption class A (in accordance with EN ISO 11654).

Certain wall surfaces may need to be fitted with sound absorbers to avoid flutter echoes.

Bearing in mind the risk of damage, the acoustic ceiling may need an impact resistant surface layer.

In spaces of more than 1500 m³ a somewhat longer reverberation time must be accepted.

In swimming pools the acoustic ceiling will also have to tolerate relatively high levels of humidity.

Play and activity rooms

Pre-schools, children's recreation centres and daycare centres are environments where children move around the whole premises. Activities range from sitting still and listening to someone reading to noisy games.

- Large open areas encourage conversation at a distance, which results in people tending to raise their voices and trying to be heard over others. Sound breeds sound, creating a disturbing "cocktail of noise".

- Hard surface materials create problematic sound amplification and sound propagation. The sound is transported a long way and so disturbs a large number of people.

- Hard flooring creates noisy footsteps and scraping noises from chairs and tables.

The authorities' recommendation

No recommendations in the UK Guidelines for these areas, contained within Building Bulletin 87 (BB87), Guidelines for Environmental Design in Schools, Part A.

Note: please also refer to Building Bulletin 93, which will replace Part A of Building Bulletin 87.

Swedish Standard 02 52 68 recommends a reverberation time of 0.4 or 0.5 seconds, depending on the selected quality level. This applies to normally furnished but unoccupied rooms. The above figure is the highest recommended value for the frequency range 250 – 4,000 Hz. At 125 Hz a value 20% higher is permitted.

Ecophon's recommendation

We recommend a reverberation time of 0.4 seconds. According to the above Swedish standard, to achieve this a full acoustic ceiling is needed of sound absorption class A (in accordance with EN ISO 11654).

Certain wall surfaces may need to be fitted with sound absorbers to avoid flutter echoes.

Bearing in mind the risk of damage, the acoustic ceiling and wall absorbers may need an impact resistant surface layer.

"The results show that no matter how well we deliver the national curriculum, it is our buildings that are dictating how much pupils can hear and concentrate on their lessons."

Headteacher David Hale, the Priory School in Hampshire, England

A few good examples

Here are just some of the educational facilities around the world that demonstrate a conscious focus on creating a good indoor environment adapted to the work they do.

In most cases the required level for the sound environment was set early in the planning stage, with rooms receiving acoustic ceilings of the top absorption class.

In other cases acoustic ceilings had to be installed at a later stage when it was found that poor acoustics were making effective teaching and learning impossible.

One of the examples, Linåker school in Sweden (page 148), describes how improving sound absorption at the lower frequencies particularly benefits pupils with impaired hearing.

Daycare centre chooses building materials with the indoor environment in mind

Environmentally friendly and adapted to allergy sufferers, Reveljen daycare centre in Umeå, Sweden looks like any other. The difference is that right from the planning stage of the building process, the greatest possible consideration has been given to children with some sort of hypersensitivity such as asthma, hay fever, eczema and other allergies.

The main aim of the Reveljen daycare centre:
"On the basis of previous knowledge and experience, to build an environmentally friendly daycare centre in which as many known allergenic factors as possible are eliminated and a good indoor climate is created."

It is suspected that a combination of sealed buildings, poor ventilation and building materials that emit hazardous substances into the air, are contributory factors to increased sensitivity in children. Poorly dried out building parts and badly thought-out designs lead to damp and fungal problems. It was therefore necessary to come up with engineering solutions and building materials that provide a healthy indoor environment. It is most important that the children's environment is as free as possible from allergenic substances.

Requirements and targets for the indoor environment were set out in a planning document. Values were laid down for levels of carbon dioxide, formaldehyde, radon daughters and aspergillus fungus and electromagnetic field strength. Fibres and particles, hair, mites and pollen were also to be kept to the lowest possible levels.

"The children feel better here than at home"

After five years operating the Reveljen daycare centre, the head comments:

"The children in the sanitised, clean areas develop resistance and gain a higher allergy threshold, handling dust, perfume and pollen better. Several of the children even feel better at the daycare centre than at home. It has been the case that children have had allergic reactions during the weekend but have got better during the week with us."

Building materials have been selected with a strong focus on avoiding irritating substances such as organic solvents, formaldehyde, softening agents in plastic, strong smells, etc.

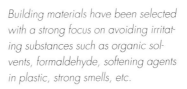

Clear role of room acoustics for learning and concentration

The Priory School in Hampshire in the UK was one of the first schools to take part in a study of classroom acoustics carried out by Heriot-Watt University in Edinburgh. The school was built to take 155 pupils aged 5 – 11.

Built in 1850, the Priory School has recently undergone major changes. The school was chosen for the study because it has an interesting mixture of different types of school building. The original school was a Victorian flint building and the new 1990s classrooms have been designed in the same style, with vaulted ceilings and high windows. Unfortunately the high ceilings, combined with the lively classrooms, caused acoustic problems for teachers and pupils alike. The school also had pre-fabricated temporary buildings.

In order to measure the acoustic improvements that could be achieved in a Victorian classroom, a suspended acoustic ceiling was installed. Measurements by Heriot-Watt University following installation showed a drop in reverberation time and background noise.

However, the improvements caused a problem: all the children and teachers wanted to work in this one room, which became known as the school's "acoustic classroom".

As a direct consequence of the study, the school is now working on a programme to ensure an improved sound environment throughout the school.

Headteacher David Hale is convinced that good acoustics in the school have a considerable impact on education and children's comprehension, a view supported by the study at Heriot-Watt University. He says:

"The study at our school was carried out during normal working days. Although we knew that our older buildings had a poor sound environment, we had no idea how large the problem was. The results show that no matter how well we deliver the national curriculum, it is our buildings that are dictating how much pupils can hear and concentrate on their lessons."

"We want to provide our pupils with the best possible conditions for learning"

The local education authority in Hampshire is showing the way to achieve good classroom acoustics. Don Allen, Chairman of Hampshire County Council's Education Committee, says:

"We are pleased with the improvements made in a number of Hampshire schools and we've decided to continue the renovation programme."

"Further studies of room acoustics are a vital tool for improving the classroom environment."

Two years after the Heriot-Watt study, all but one of the classrooms have had an acoustic ceiling fitted to create a pleasant learning environment which maximises pupils' learning.

Newly renovated school needs acoustic solutions

Renovated in 1998, Mønsted school in Viborg, Denmark, has 245 pupils and 22 teachers. After the renovations many teachers complained about the noise and poor acoustics in many parts of the school.

The worst problem was the sound environment in the gymnasium and the home economics rooms. Sound echoed around the gymnasium, making it difficult for pupils to hear what was being said and forcing them to raise their voices to be heard over the noise. The teachers often had a headache after lessons. There was a similar problem in the home economics rooms, where the acoustics were so poor that the smallest scrape of a kitchen utensil caused unnecessarily disturbing noise. The pupils had difficulty concentrating, were poor listeners and used up a lot of energy raising their voices.

With this in mind, the school management decided to install an acoustic ceiling in the areas in which the problems were greatest. Major emphasis was placed on using acoustic solutions tailored to the needs of the school and to the available budget.

After the acoustic ceilings and wall absorbers were installed, teachers found it much easier to relax and concentrate. The gymnasium became quieter and calmer and great improvements were seen in the home economics department. Pupils stopped shouting in the gymnasium and working with kitchen utensils was no longer felt to be noisy during home economics lessons. The pupils no longer raise their voices and it has become much easier to attract attention.

The pupils themselves also noticed the improvements. They asked what had actually been done to the rooms, which they felt now had "a completely different sound".

In the staffroom several teachers used to complain that they could not relax between lessons because of the background noise from the neighbouring corridors. They also found it difficult to concentrate when involved in lesson preparation.

Areas with mobile activities and a lot of noise from equipment, e.g. kitchens for home economics teaching, always require an acoustic ceiling of absorption class A.

Gymnasium with acoustic ceiling installed after renovations.

French auditorium with world-class acoustics

Dijon in France has a music centre that many consider to have one of the world's best sound environments. Great care went into the room acoustics and sound insulation and aesthetic considerations also played a key role when the architects created this modern cultural facility.

A judicious mixture of steel and concrete has created a building with a clear identity and strong character.

In the large concert hall, the requirement was laid down that even the softest of musical sounds must be able to be discerned by the audience. Therefore, all installations that generate sound had their noise damped. The facilities are mainly intended for musical events, but are sometimes also used for teaching.

Next to the concert hall lie several other music rooms and activity areas that represent a major risk of sound spreading from room to room. Careful sound insulation has allowed external noise from sources such as cars, trains and planes to be blocked out. The ingenious building principle of rooms within rooms has lead to a structurally separated design which prevents sound propagation through walls and joists.

In the areas in which noise needed damping, the architects and acoustics experts worked closely to achieve the best possible room acoustics. They agreed that an invisible suspension system would provide the most aesthetic solution for the room, as well as providing excellent acoustics. The interior, which is often fully visible from outside, also has an impact on the whole exterior and the street outside. Other parts of the building, such as the corridors, have acoustic ceilings where the suspension system has been kept visible as a clear element of the ceiling.

Teaching music places major demands on acoustics.

The auditorium in Dijon has a bold and exclusive interior in which the ceiling has been given a dominant aesthetic function.

Office building converted into a modern college

As soon as they saw the 1950's office block, architects at De Jong Gortemaker in the Netherlands realised the great opportunities for preserving the character of large parts of the building in conjunction with conversion to a college. The only addition to the building were the lecture theatres. The property, which belongs to University College Utrecht, the Netherlands, has a total of 2,500 staff and 28,000 students.

A number of architectural features from the 1950 s such as the entrance with its oriel, the elegant spiral stairs and the canteen at the top have been preserved.

The initial aim was to create a teaching building with flexible spaces and a variation of classrooms and study areas. Open and closed rooms were created for individual study and group work, for concentration and for discussions. When the dividing walls were taken down, the previous transparent environment was revealed with its wonderful light and was able to be compared with photographs of the building in its original condition. Adapting the building to its new educational function led to the traditional central corridor being placed against the outer wall to make room for spacious teaching premises.

The goal from the start was to exploit the height of the room using ceiling islands and it was decided to maintain the existing ventilation system. However, it became clear that from an aesthetic point of view it was better to conceal the installations with a complete suspended ceiling.

As far as possible sound damping surface layers were chosen for the flooring, which creates a calm and quiet environment in combination with the acoustic ceiling.

The college has adapted its operations to modern IT and the new style of study focusing on individuality, project-based self-study and group work. The new trend requires quiet rooms with plenty of space. The infrastructure of the college building is being changed and long corridors with classrooms are being converted into a teaching landscape for flexible forms of study.

A spacious multimedia resource centre was created in the centre of the building.

The corridors are not only transport routes. They also offer great opportunities for individual study in good light, with noise reduced by building dividing walls and installing a full acoustic ceiling.

A good sound environment essential when teaching languages

As the population in the suburbs of Gdynia in Poland increases, new schools are constantly needed in the area to ensure that children do not have too far to travel. It was therefore decided to convert a barracks-like school building into a new comprehensive school and new grammar school. Major resources were put into the working environment, not least room acoustics.

"All our visitors are impressed by the sound environment of the school. The most frequent comment is about the low noise level during break-time," says Pawel Morawski, deputy head of the educational units that form part of general school complex no. 15. The clear difference between this school and others is often mentioned. Morawski says that the school staff find the noise level low, which also affects their pupils, who appear to behave more quietly and calmly than pupils of the same age at other schools.

"No form of sound amplification is needed in rooms with acoustic ceilings, not even when many listeners are gathered together, for example at parents' evenings. Our radio broadcasts in the school also function better in these premises."

"This sound environment makes it easy to forget that you are in a school," adds Morawski. As a teacher of languages including English, he emphasises the major impact of room acoustics on learning a foreign language. Comparing the classrooms with the new acoustic ceiling with the place he used to work, the biggest difference he notices is in the quality of the sound from the tape recorder.

The worn-out old school building went through a complete transformation. Most of the buildings were totally rebuilt, partly because a new school reform required the site not only to offer education for comprehensive school pupils but also for upper secondary school students. The old library and main hall were converted into ordinary classrooms.

"For me as a language teacher, it is vital to be heard in all parts of the room when reading a text. Good acoustics are essential to understanding the language we are learning," concludes a very happy Morawski.

The architect behind the building, Adam Drochomiercki, believes that the acoustic ceilings offer a combination of interesting solutions with good sound absorbing properties. The ceilings, with their special surface layer, proved excellent for use in the school's main hall, corridors and sports hall.

University canteen with acoustic ceilings at various levels

In conjunction with the renovation of the canteen at the University of Rhode Island in the US, the older ceiling was replaced with a suspended acoustic ceiling. The ceiling was installed at different levels and was shaped into curves to fit in with the aesthetic values and to hide an extensive system of ducting for the new air conditioning system. The premises covering approximately 1,200 m² received a considerable facelift in the form of a new acoustic ceiling, new lighting and repainted walls.

The educational establishment that is now the University of Rhode Island was built in 1888 and over the years has expanded into several new buildings. One of these is Butterfield Hall, a single storey building with a flat roof and large glass surfaces. The building was constructed in 1959 partly to house the canteen at a time when there was usually no mechanical ventilation system.

In 1999 renovation work to install an air conditioning system started on the building in partnership with architects Saccoccio and Associates. As the unit required a great deal of space and as there was a desire to improve the aesthetics of the canteen, a new suspended ceiling was considered. An acoustic ceiling was found that provided an attractive aesthetic transition between different ceiling levels.

The university's chief architect, Don Krasko, took part in the renovation work and found that the ceiling also had the durable and hardwearing characteristics needed in a university building. He also appreciated the fact that this type of acoustic ceiling can be dismantled, cleaned and replaced, something not possible with the old ceiling.

As well as wanting to hide installations in the ceiling, those involved recognised the value of considerably improving the sound environment within the building.

The canteen also has areas used for meetings, which requires limiting sound propagation.

"The curved ceiling panels gave the building an attractive appearance and we managed to turn a potential problem of ceilings with different levels into an advantage. The dining hall was converted into a pleasant dining area."

Architect Victor LaPerche, Saccoccio and Associates

"Less noise and better acoustics make eating a more enjoyable experience for our students."

Don Krasko, chief architect, University of Rhode Island

A full acoustic ceiling hides installations in the ceiling of the canteen and improves the sound environment for staff and guests.

Reverberation time more than halved

Patterson River College in Carrum, outside Melbourne, Australia, has considerably improved room acoustics and speech intelligibility in one if its classrooms. The sound environment was tested before and after the acoustic improvements were carried out.

First the background noise levels were measured in six different places within the room and three different situations: when pupils were quiet, when they were speaking and when the teacher was teaching. The reverberation time was tested from four different positions, with and without pupils in the room.

As with the reverberation time, speech intelligibility (STI, Speech Transmission Index) was measured before and after an acoustic ceiling was installed. First a reading was taken without any speech in the room and then with the normal background noise of the pupils.

The room, originally used as a laboratory, is 10.9 metres long, 8.2 metres wide and 3.35 metres high, with a podium at the front for the teacher. The ceiling was clad in a hard material initially and the furniture comprised steel desks with laminate tops and steel chairs with plastic seats. The study showed the room to be dominated by hard, reflective surfaces.

An acoustic ceiling was installed to improve the sound environment. Measurements showed that this reduced the general noise level in the room. Without the acoustic ceiling the reverberation time was 1.4 seconds in the middle frequencies, a long way above the Australian standard (0.6 – 0.7 seconds). After installing the acoustic ceiling, the figure dropped to 0.6 seconds, within the required limits.

According to Peter Pirozek, who produced the acoustics report, "the teachers think the room is now one of the best rooms in the school and they all agree that the acoustics are much better."

Mr Robert Stephens, head of Patterson River College, comments, "the new acoustic ceiling is a real asset for teachers using the classroom and for pupils' learning. The difference between the old ceiling and the new acoustic ceiling is unbelievable and echo and noise have fallen dramatically."

The reverberation time was measured in the classroom,
with and without an acoustic ceiling.

New approach great for the sound environment

Linåker school in Svalöv in Sweden was built in 1970 and renovated between 1999 and 2000. During these changes there was a particular focus on improving the sound environment, with a new approach to room acoustics being introduced. The interior in general received a total makeover.

A trial room was built first to test the results of the improvements, before moving on to the other rooms in the school.

The results after lessons in the trial room over a period of a year were very positive. The air quality was better, the room was brighter with good lighting, a more even temperature and a background noise level within the requirements of building standards.

The acoustic ceiling tested was based on a new method of installing extra thick sound absorbers just where the ceiling met the walls in order to reduce sound reflection from the corners. The test proved to be a great success. Measurements in the trial room showed more or less the same short reverberation time of less than 0.5 seconds for all speech frequencies, even those in the low frequencies which are usually difficult to hear. For someone with impaired hearing these frequencies are extra important for the best possible speech intelligibility.

The modest extra cost of creating an improved sound environment will pay for itself several times over as there is no need to provide extra resources for hearing-impaired pupils.

After all these positive results, it was decided that all the school's classrooms would be built according to the new principles. Today almost all the areas have been renovated, including corridors, communal areas, the library, offices and study rooms. This has created consistent room acoustics so that pupils can keep their voices down to the same low level wherever they are in the school.

Nils Ingvar Ekholm, AB Svalövsbostäder in Skåne, Southern Sweden, says:

"Since the school was built thirty years ago, we have learnt about the working environment problems suffered by schools from that time. We started by rebuilding one of the rooms to achieve the best possible working environment – a new ventilation and heating system, better light in the form of uplighters and a reflective white ceiling, new, lighter flooring, light-coloured walls and a newly developed acoustic ceiling. We took down the old ceiling which was absorption class D and replaced it with a suspended acoustic ceiling in absorption class A. A further reduction in the reverberation time for the low frequencies was achieved by installing extra thick sound absorbers above the acoustic ceiling."

Sound absorption has been improved in the classrooms and is now also suitable for people with impaired hearing.

"In our case, we wanted to bring the reverberation time down to a level low enough for us to be able to teach hearing-impaired pupils here. Our requirements were therefore much more demanding than the authorities' standards. But I'm convinced that if things are good for people with a hearing impairment, then they are good for the whole school. We reduced background noise considerably using the acoustic ceiling and a quieter ventilation system."

Communal areas, corridors and most other rooms have been fitted with an acoustic ceiling to achieve consistent room acoustics.

HM Queen Elizabeth opened the school of the future in the UK

The Admiral Lord Nelson School is designed to look like a ship facing out to sea.

The school was built as a great example of the future of school buildings in the UK. Shape, colour and design have been used to create an environment that has a positive impact on learning and the rooms have been designed to make communication between individuals easier. However, achieving this demands a great deal of the sound environment, an issue which has been taken very seriously.

The school was opened by HM Queen Elizabeth II in 1998.

Headteacher Dianne Smith, who had many comments to make about the environment of the new school, is happy to share her experience of successfully taming noise and creating good speech intelligibility in an open school environment.

"When I first saw the proposal for a school with an open-plan designed mall area, I was instantly worried that noise could be a problem," explains Dianne Smith. "The poor experience I and my staff had in the old classic Victorian school buildings shows how important acoustics issues are in a learning environment. But when the school was finished the acoustics were excellent. Even the large main hall has a quiet and calm atmosphere."

"I myself have impaired hearing which makes it difficult to hear what the children say, so classrooms are a particular problem for me. In our new rooms, the great acoustics have helped me in two ways. I can be heard and I can hear what pupils say – people repeating themselves is simply unnecessary. This is crucial for creating an excellent environment for both teaching and learning."

The same standards that one would demand of a well-functioning office environment have been applied to the function and pleasantness of the school, to achieve a successful and comfortable educational environment. This excellent learning and teaching environment, with its good acoustics, helps to avoid adverse effects such as voice strain, teacher absenteeism, and misbehaving pupils. Since the opening of the school, teachers and staff have continued to praise their new working environment.

"It's a wonderful environment, a warm and inviting place. The good acoustics really help to create a calmer environment."

"On one occasion visitors to the school thought the school was empty because it was so quiet."

The acoustic ceilings' superb ability to improve the sound environment put an end to concerns about a noisy environment at the Admiral Lord Nelson School.

"Background noise has been reduced and speech can be heard more clearly."

"Being able to hear is a key element of language training. Our classroom has practically no echo, which would otherwise mean people having to strain their voices unnecessarily. We can now lower the volume when listening to our language tapes. Good acoustics have created a calmer atmosphere in the class and, above all, the grades for our national tests using tapes have risen."

The school is really unique in that the practical working environment issues which directly affect teachers and students have been integrated into the planning of the school. Every room has been individually designed to suit the end user. What could have been an extremely noisy environment is really quiet.

And a final word from Dianne Smith:

"There is no doubt that the noise level in a school affects learning and discipline. If children can't hear what is being said, they become more inclined to talk to their friends. That's why it is vital to create a calm environment."

Acoustic improvements put everyone in a good mood

When the new development of the Kindergarten Am Zauberwald in Walkenried, Germany, was finished in 2000, something was not right – the extremely high noise levels.

Extending the kindergarten was necessary to provide space for all the 75 children – who are divided into three different groups. In addition to three large play and activity rooms, the basement level has an open kitchen area with a "children's cafeteria" and storage and cleaning areas. The top floor comprises a flexible facility with built-in children's kitchen, used for various physical exercises and creative activities, an office and staff rooms.

The aim of the kindergarten's pedagogical approach is to teach children to become independent and develop into individuals full of self-confidence. They get to try new things and create their own experiences. However, structure and management are necessary to meet the requirements for order, safety and the aim of the education, which is why there is a fixed plan for the various activities of the day.

This ought to have been enough to meet the requirements for an ideal environment in which children could play and learn, but the first thing staff noticed when they moved into the new premises was the noise level. The noise came from the children's various activities, games, play and exercise. The children and teachers suffered headaches and ringing in their ears. Concentration dropped dramatically and the children became unruly.

The complaints were quick to appear. Parents noted that children raised their voices when they were at the kindergarten. It could take the whole weekend before their voices were back to their normal level.

The acoustics were found to be at the root of the problem, so the rooms in which the children spent their time were fitted with acoustic ceilings of the top absorption class. Building physics expert Friedel Reinhold of the company Ingenieur- und Sachverständigengesellschaft für Bauphysik, who was involved in the decision, found that the positive subjective assessments of the new sound environment were supported by the objective measurements of reverberation time.

After the improvements to the sound environment, the happy and relaxed faces of staff and children were plain to see. Now further acoustics improvements are being carried out where needed.

As the head of the nursery school says: "Now peace and happiness reign again in our nursery. Before you couldn't even hold a normal conversation with someone a metre away."

Bibliography

Airey, Sharon (2000). *Education.* Paper/Airey. (in English)

Andersson, Johnny (1998). *Akustik & buller: en praktisk handbok (Acoustics and noise – a practical handbook).* AB Svensk Byggtjänst. (in Swedish)

Berglund, Birgitta & Lindvall, Thomas (edited by) (1995). *Community Noise.* Stockholm University and Karolinska Institute/World Health Organization, Archives of the Center for Sensory Research, Volume 2, Issue 1, 1995. (in English)

Bilsom, (now Dalloz Safety) (1981). *När, var och hur vi hör (When, where and how we hear).* Brochure/Dalloz Safety. (in Swedish)

Bodén, Hans & Carlsson, Ulf & Glav, Ragnar & Wallin, H.P. & Åbom, Mats (1999). *Ljud och vibrationer (Sound and Vibrations).* Kungliga Tekniska Högskolan, Institutionen för Farkostteknik, Marcus Wallenberg Laboratoriet för Ljud- och Vibrationsforskning (Royal Institute of Technology, Department of Vehicle Engineering, Marcus Wallenberg Laboratory for Sound and Vibration Research). (in Swedish)

Bodin, Anders (2000). *Om byggprocessen (About the building process).* Paper/Bodin. (in Swedish)

Boverket & Arbetarskyddsstyrelsen (The Swedish National Board of Building, Planning and Housing & The Swedish National Board of Occupational Health) (edited by Hellberg, Annika) (1996). *Att se, höra och andas i skolan: en handbok om skolans innemiljö (Seeing, hearing and breathing in schools – a handbook on the indoor environment of schools).* Publikationsservice. (in Swedish)

Byggforskningsrådet (Swedish Building Research Council)/Andersson, Sven & Borg, Thomas & Djurstedt, Bengt & Gulliksson, Hans & Igelström, Leif & Jonson, Jan-Olof & Lindstam, Martin & Olsson, Stefan & Starby, Lars (1992). *Bra innemiljö i skolan (Good indoor environments in schools).* Byggforskningsrådet/Förlagshuset Gothia. (in Swedish)

Börjesson, Lena (1992). *ABC-bok om lärande (ABC of learning).* Metoda. (in Swedish)

Crandell, C. Carl (1993). *Speech Recognition in Noise by Children with Minimal Degrees of Sensorineural Hearing Loss.* Ear & Hearing, Vol. 14, No. 3, 1993. (in English)

Department for Education and Employment (DfEE) (1997). *Guidelines for environmental design in schools, Building Bulletin 87 (BB87).* DfEE. (in English)

Ecophon (1998). *Ljud och det moderna kontoret (Sound and the Modern Office).* Ecophon. (in Swedish, English, Dutch, French, German, Danish, Polish)

Encyclopædia Britannica

Evans, Gary W. & Bullinger, Monika & Hygge, Staffan (1995). *Chronic noise and psychological stress.* Psychological Science, Vol. 6, No. 6, Nov 1995. (in English)

Evans, Gary W. & Bullinger, Monika & Hygge, Staffan (1998). *Chronic noise exposure and psychological response: A prospective study of children living under environmental stress.* Psychological Science, Vol. 9, No. 1, Jan 1998. (in English)

Folkhälsoinstitutets allergiprogram (1999). (Swedish National Institute of Public Health's allergy programme). *Ren luft på kontoret (Clean air in the office).* Alprosen (4/99) Folkhälsoinstitutet. (in Swedish)

Folkhälsoinstitutet (Swedish National Institute of Public Health) (2000). *De sex stegen för en sund skola: vägledning om innemiljö vid planering och förvaltning (Six steps for a healthy school: a guide on the indoor environment in planning and building management).* Förlagshuset Gothia. (in Swedish and English)

Gage, N. L. & Berliner, David C. (1998). *Educational psychology.* Houghton Mifflin. (in English)

Hannaford, Carla (1998). *Lär med hela kroppen: inlärning sker inte bara i huvudet (Smart moves).* Brain Books. (in Swedish and English)

Harris, Sten (interview with audiology specialist Dr Harris, associate professor and head of department at Lund University Hospital, Sweden, 1995)

Holm, Birgitta & Hult, Marie (1999). *Projekteringsguide för en god innemiljö i skolor – förstudie (Planning guide for good indoor environments in schools – preliminary study).* Byggforskningsrådet (Swedish Building Research Council). (in Swedish)

Hellström, Björn (1999). *Akustisk design vad är det? (What is acoustic design?)* Bygg & Teknik, 3/99. (in Swedish)

Ising, H & Braun, C. (2000). *Acute and chronic endocrine effects of noise: Review of the research conducted at the Institute for Water, Soil and Air Hygiene.* Noise & Health 2000;7,7-24. (in English)

Kirke-, utdannings- og forskningsdepartementet (Norwegian Ministry of Education, Research and Church Affairs) (1995). *Skoleanlegg – forbedring og fornyelse. Grunnskole, videregående opplæring og voksenopplæring (Schools – improvement and renewal).* Kommuneforlaget. (in Norwegian)

Kjellberg, Anders m fl (1993). Forskning & Praktik 4/1993. (in Swedish)

Kjellberg, Anders (1990). *Inte bara hörselskador (Not only hearing impairment)*. Arbetslivsinstitutet (National Institute for Working Life), 1990:36. (in Swedish)

Laike, Torbjörn (1997). *The impact of daycare environments on children's mood and behaviour*. Scandinavian Journal of Psychology, 1997, 38, 209-218. (in English)

Landström, Ulf & Arlinger, Stig & Hygge, Staffan & Johansson, Örjan & Kjellberg, Anders & Persson Waye, Kerstin (1999). *Störande buller: Kunskapsöversikt för kriteriedokumentation (Disturbing noise: Survey of criteria documentation)*. Arbetslivsinstitutet (National Institute for Working Life), 1999:27. (in Swedish)

Lerner, Thomas (2000). *Skolan stressar eleverna (School makes students stressed)*. Dagens Nyheter 2000-02-24. (in Swedish)

Luthman, Gösta et al (ed.) (1969). *Handbok i ergonomi (Handbook on ergonomics)*. Almqvist & Wiksell. (in Swedish)

Lys & Optik/Lysteknisk Selskab ([Delta division for] Light & Optics/Danish Illumination Engineering Society) (1993). *God og energirigtig skolebelysning (Good energy-efficient school lighting)*. Lysteknisk Selskab. (in Danish)

MacKenzie, David J. (2000). *Classroom acoustics*. Paper/MacKenzie. (in English)

Mackenzie, David J. & Airey, Sharon (1999). *Classroom acoustics – a research project: Summary report*. Heriot-Watt University, Edinburgh, Scotland. (in English)

Maltén, Arne (1999). *Vad är kunskap? (What is knowledge?)* Gleerups Förlag. (in Swedish)

Maxwell, Lorraine E. & Evans, Gary W. (2000). *The effects of noise on preschool children's pre-reading skills*. Journal of Environmental Psychology, 2000, 20, 91-97. (in English)

Mulhern, James (1959). *A history of education: a social interpretation*. The Ronald Press Company. (in English)

Nabelek AK & Donahue AM (1984). *Perceptions of consonants in reverberation by native and non-native listeners*. Journal of the Acoustical Society of America, 75, 632-34, 1984. (in English)

Nationalencyklopedin (Swedish National Encyclopedia) (1998-). Bra Böcker. (in Swedish)

Norinder, Eva (interview with Eva Norinder, teacher of the hearing-impaired, Göteborg, Sweden, 1999)

NUTEK (Swedish National Board for Industrial and Technical Development) (1994). *Programkrav, belysning i skolor: Programkrav för god och energieffektiv belysning i skolor (Programme requirements for lighting in schools)*. NUTEK, Effektivare energianvändning. (in Swedish)

OECD (Organisation for Economic Co-operation and Development)/Centre for Educational Research and Innovation Indicators of Education Systems (2000). *Education at a glance: OECD indicators*. OECD. (in English)

Onciul, Julia von (1996). *ABC of Work Related Disorders: Stress at work*. British Medical Journal, 1996;313:745-748 (21 Sept). (in English)

Palladio, Andrea (1570/1983). *Fyra böcker om arkitekturen (Four books on architecture)*. Vinga Bokförlag. (original 1570, this edition 1983) (original in Italian, in Swedish)

Pedersen, Odd & Svantesson, Bo (1976). *Undervisningsteknologi: Utbildningsplanering och samhälle (Educational techniques: Planning education and society)*. LiberLäromedel. (in Swedish)

Rasmussen, Steen Eiler (1999). *Experience architecture*. MIT Press. (in English)

Royal Institute for the Deaf and Hard of Hearing

Ruhe, Carsten (2000). *Kommunikationsräume*. Paper/Ruhe. (in German)

Sandström, Carl Ivar (1989). *Utbildningens idéhistoria (The history of ideas of education)*. Svensk Facklitteratur. (in Swedish)

Schick, August & Meis, Markus & Reckhardt, Carsten (edited by) (2000). *Contributions to Psychological Acoustics; Results of the eighth Oldenburg symposium on psychological acoustics*. Bibliotheks- und Informationssystem der Universität Oldenburg. (in English)

Standardiseringen i Sverige (SIS) (Swedish Standards Institution) (2001). *SS 02 52 68 – Byggakustik – Ljudklassning av utrymmen i byggnader – Vårdlokaler, undervisningslokaler, dag- och fritidshem, kontor och hotell (Acoustics – Sound classification of spaces in buildings – institutional premises, rooms for education, day centres and after school centres, rooms for office work and hotels)*. SIS. (in Swedish)

Steinberg, John M. (1998). *Låt skolan dö – länge leve lärandet! (The Death of Schooling – Long Live Learning!)* Ekelund (in Swedish)

Svenska Kommunförbundet (Swedish Association of Local Authorities) & Fahlin, Per & Andersson, Sven (1997). *Upphandling av sunda hus: redovisning av erfarenheter från Malmö stad samt ett 50-tal kommuner och landsting (The procurement process of healthy buildings).* Svenska Kommunförbundet. (in Swedish)

Synskadades Riksförbund (The Swedish Association of the Visually Impaired)

Söderberg, Jan (1992). *Byggnadsekonomi; Byggprocessen i samhället (Building economics, the building process in society).* Institutionen för byggnadsekonomi, Lunds Tekniska Högskola (Department of Construction Management, Lund Institute of Technology, Sweden). (in Swedish)

Thomas, Robert Murray (edited by) (1990). *International comparative education: practise, issues and prospects.* Pergamon Press. (in English)

Weinstein, Neil D. (1974). *Effect of noise on intellectual performance.* Journal of Applied Psychology, 1974, Vol. 59, No. 5, 548-554. (in English)

Yap Sau Hee (1999). *Good acoustics will help teachers.* The Straits Times (Singapore), December 18, 1999. (in English)

Photographs and illustrations

Ecophon has been developing, manufacturing and marketing acoustic ceilings and wall absorbers since the 1950s. Our mission is to help create a working environment that is pleasant on the eye, ear and mind. We have our headquarters in Hyllinge, just east of Helsingborg, in Sweden, and are established in the UK, Denmark, Finland, Poland, Germany, the Netherlands, France, the Czech Republic, Russia, the US and China. We are also represented across the rest of the world. Why not visit our website at www.ecophon.co.uk

Ecophon®
ACOUSTIC CEILINGS